Science 1

Elaine Chantler

Acknowledgements

I would like to offer my grateful thanks to the head teacher Anne Siggins and the staff and pupils of Priory Fields Primary School, Dover, in particular to Ruth Bishop for her time and effort in creating displays for this book, you are a superstar!

My thanks also go to Liz Madge, Myles Kearney, Andrew Berry (Kent Advisory Service), Chris Martin, Zoë Parish and Steve Forest.

I would like to dedicate this book to my wonderful mum Margaret.

The publishers would also like to thank Horsendale Primary School for their artwork on page 72.

From Sound & Hearing on page 44

Commissioning Editor: Zoë Parish   Editor: Christine Graham   Cover Design: Sophie Pelham

Page Layout: Barbara Linton   Photography: Steve Forest   Illustrations: Martin Pierce

First published in 2008 by Belair Publications.

Every effort has been made to trace the copyright holders of material used in this publication. If any copyright holder has been overlooked, we should be pleased to make the necessary arrangements.

British Library Cataloguing in Publication Data. A catalogue record for this publication is available from the British Library.

ISBN 978-1-84191-461-9

Contents

Ourselves	4
Materials	16
Growing Plants	28
Sound & Hearing	40
Light & Dark	52
Pushes & Pulls	64
Assessment Ideas	76
Self-Assessment Sheets	78

Ourselves

These grids demonstrate the learning objectives covered in the activities within the theme. The curriculum references indicate the relevant programme of study (PoS) for a subject area unless otherwise stated.

	Learning Objectives	Curriculum References
Science (Page 6)		
Scientific Enquiry	Plan and conduct investigations using the five senses.	Sc1/1
	Use knowledge and understanding to draw and explain conclusions about food and the senses.	Sc1/2a-j
Life Processes and Living Things (QCA Science Unit 1A)	Understand that living things feed, grow, and have senses. Use the Internet for research about internal and external organs.	Sc2/1b; ICT PoS 1a;2a
	Recognise and compare external body parts. Begin to understand internal body parts such as bones.	Sc2/2a,b
	Look at the food journey and the impact of diet on the body.	Sc2/2c
	Understand that we use our senses to make sense of the world that we live in.	Sc2/2g
	Use a digital camera to make a record of the differences between ourselves and others.	Sc2/4a; ICT PoS 2b;5b
Literacy (Page 8)		
Drama	Use language to explore and create familiar situations in a health centre role play area.	En1/4a
Understanding and Interpreting Texts	Read fiction titles about the body.	En2/2a
Word Structure and Spelling	Discuss, read and list key words about the body.	En2/1f,j
Text Structure and Organisation	Use familiar fiction texts about the body as a model for creative writing.	En3/1f
	Collaboratively write a book about the body, using the organisational features of a non-fiction text.	En3/1d,f
Creating and Shaping Texts	Write labels, captions and descriptions about the body.	En3/2a-c
	Write instructional text about how a body grows.	En3/1e;2c,d
Mathematics (Page 10)		
Knowing and Using Number Facts	Use body parts to create and describe number patterns when counting on in steps of two.	Ma2/2b
Using and Applying Mathematics	Choose and use appropriate strategies to solve problems about calculating the size of feet and about calculating height.	Ma2/1a-c
Measuring	Select and use appropriate equipment when measuring parts of the body.	Ma3/4a,c
Handling Data	Use data-handling software to produce lists, tables and charts to sort and organise information about the features of the children.	Ma2/5a; ICT PoS 3a

Learning Objectives	Curriculum References
RE (Page 12)	
Explore creation stories in a variety of religions.	PoS 1a;3f
PSHCE (Page 12)	
Talk about showing care and concern for others and ourselves.	PoS 4a-e
Discuss diet as part of a healthy lifestyle.	PoS 3a; Sc2/2c
Discuss how to keep our bodies clean.	PoS 3b,e
Talk about road safety and other safety issues in the local area.	PoS 3g
Design & Technology (Page 14)	
Develop ideas to create a photo frame for a picture of their family and a special keepsake box.	PoS 1a-e;2c,d
Select and use tools, techniques and materials to create a moving model of themselves.	QCA D&T Unit 1A; PoS 2a,c,d
History (Page 14)	
Place familiar objects from today and the past in chronological order.	QCA History Unit 1A; PoS 1a,b
Use books, the Internet and other sources to identify differences in ways of life for children today and those in the past.	PoS 2b;4a; ICT PoS 1a
Geography (Page 14)	
Draw pictures of homes in the local area.	QCA Geography Unit 1; PoS 1b;4a
Use appropriate geographical vocabulary to describe where they live.	PoS 2a
Use and draw maps of the local area and use Internet maps to plot where they live.	PoS 2c,e; ICT PoS 1a
Use pictures and photographs to point out features of the environment around the school.	PoS 2d;3a
PE (Page 15)	
Explore a variety of skills and actions using the body.	PoS 1a;3a
Explore changes in rhythm, speed, level and direction of movement.	PoS 6b
Music (Page 15)	
Sing songs about the body.	PoS 1a
Explore sounds that can be made using body parts.	PoS 2a,b;4c
Art (Page 15)	
Use the Internet to find famous self-portraits and create self-portraits.	QCA Art Unit 1A; PoS 1a; ICT PoS 1a
Explore painting with body parts.	PoS 4a;5b
Experiment with portraits using a digital camera.	ICT PoS 2b;5b
Evaluate work and identify possible improvements.	PoS 3a,b

Science

Starting Points

- Ask the children to draw around each other on large sheets of paper and then label as many external body parts as possible. Use the activity sheet on page 7 to draw and label body parts.

Enquiry

- Discuss the role of the five senses with the children. Carry out senses investigations such as our sense of touch, using textured objects in a feely bag; test the sense of smell by using highly fragrant foods such as a pickled onion, mint, apples and cheese. These can be placed in an empty film canister and held under the nose.

- Can the children identify mystery objects in sealed containers by using their sense of hearing? Try a taste test using different flavours of crisps.

- Investigate the importance of the appearance of our food by presenting the children with mashed potato that is coloured blue with food colouring.

- Ask the children to collaborate on a large poster to illustrate our senses using pictures and objects, as shown here in the display photograph.

Extension Activities

- Use a fabric tabard with Velcro organs to explain the functions of internal organs or to follow the journey that our food takes through our bodies.

- Ask at your local hospital for unwanted X-ray images to show the children or use an Internet search engine to source X-ray images online.

- Ask the children to click and drag on-screen images and text onto a face or body outline.

What's inside me?

How much do you
know about what is
inside your body?

Draw as many
things as you can.

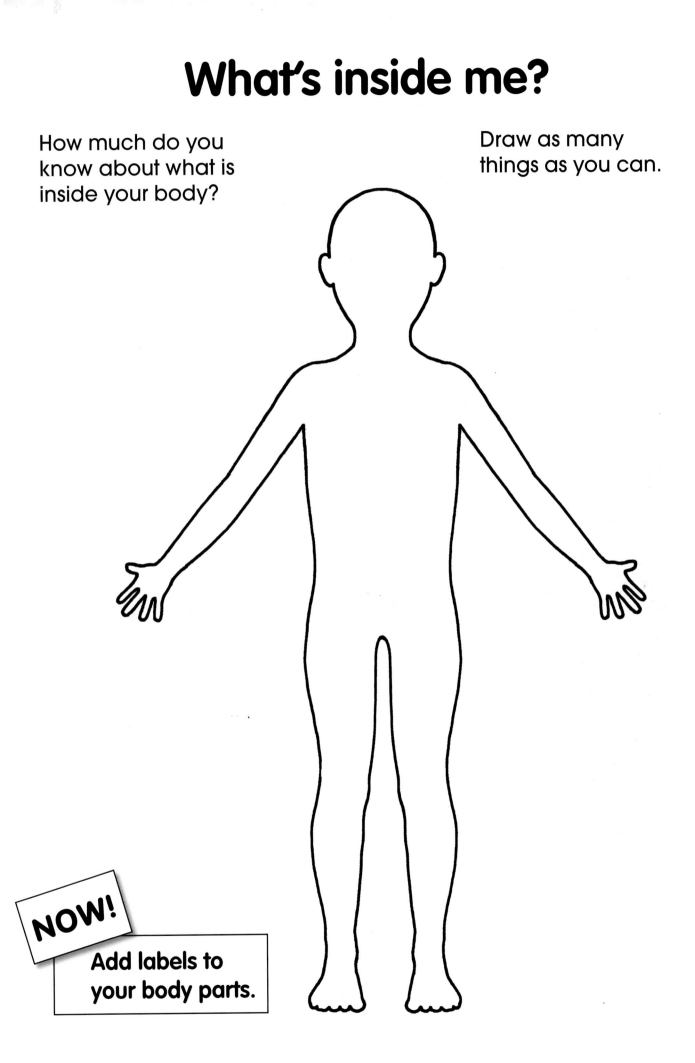

NOW!

**Add labels to
your body parts.**

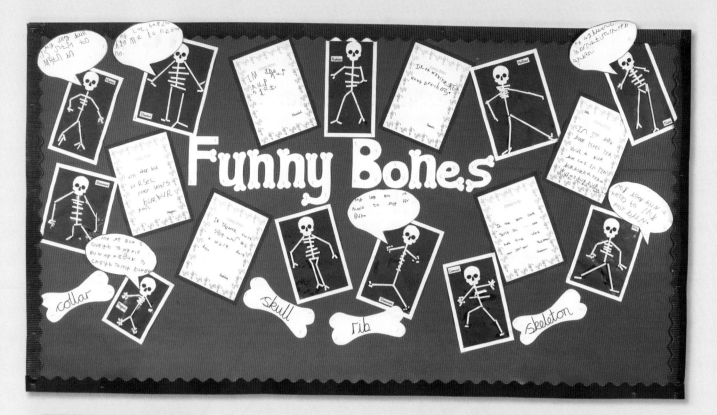

Literacy

Speaking and Listening

- Set up a themed role play area, such as a health centre or X-ray department, in the classroom.

- Sit a child in a 'hot seat' and ask them to answer questions in the role of a health care professional.

Reading and Writing

- Ask the children to write a description of a class member then play 'Guess Who?' by reading out the description and deciding who is being described.

- Write labels and captions for a classroom display about the parts of the body. Point to different bones and describe how they make up a skeleton, as shown here in the display photograph.

- Ask groups of children to produce sections for a whole-class big book about the body.

- Ask the children to write instructions for their parents entitled 'How to make me grow' and stick onto a seed packet featuring a picture of the child.

- Read fiction titles such as Funny bones by Janet and Allan Ahlberg (Picture Puffin) and use the text as a model for the children's own writing, such as describing the dark, spooky corridor or classroom.

- Read and find key 'body' topic words on a wordsearch, ask the children to create their own wordsearch on an appropriate grid.

- Ask the children to find hidden key 'body' topic words on a word grid, as illustrated on the activity sheet on page 9.

Body words wordsearch

Can you find the hidden words?

skeleton

heart

hands

leg

feet

lip

ear

nose

throat

bone

brain

ribs

elbow

eyes

toes

waist

s	y	m	h	a	n	d	s
e	b	l	e	g	u	s	k
y	o	i	a	r	e	t	e
e	n	p	r	o	l	s	l
f	e	e	t	x	b	i	e
l	q	t	h	r	o	a	t
v	n	o	s	e	w	w	o
e	a	r	b	r	a	i	n

Maths

Using and Applying

- Discuss the parts of our body that come in 2s, such as two hands, two feet, arms, legs, nostrils, ears, eyes, thumbs. Use this as an introduction to counting in 2s. Use a large one hundred grid square to investigate the pattern created when counting in 2s. Discuss odd and even numbers. Ask the children to count in 2s using parts of their body, such as hands or feet, as shown on the display and the activity sheet on page 11.

- Can the children solve a giant problem? Prepare a 1m-long cut-out footprint. Explain to the children that a giant left the footprint in your garden. Pose the question: *Is it possible to calculate the height of the giant based on the length of the footprint alone?* The children need to establish that if they can use their own footprint to calculate their own height then the same principle could be used on the giant's footprint. The children will discover that people are, approximately, the height of seven times the length of their foot and will then be able to make the calculation for the giant!

Measuring

- Ask the children to use weighing scales, metre sticks and tape measures to record weight, height and the length of body parts such as hand spans, arms and legs.

- Draw around and cut out a hand or foot shape and use as a non-standard unit of measurement for items such as classroom furniture. Discuss the problems incurred when using such units.

Handling Data

- Ask the children to produce a graph of measurement data using a package such as RM Starting Graph.

- Look at shoe sizes. Are the children with the biggest feet also the tallest children? Produce a pictogram of shoe sizes.

- Use two overlapping sorting hoops laid out on the floor to create a Venn diagram. Sort information about class members such as who has blond hair, who wears glasses, who has size 12 shoes.

Counting in twos

Draw rings around the pairs of body parts and
find the total number by counting up in twos.

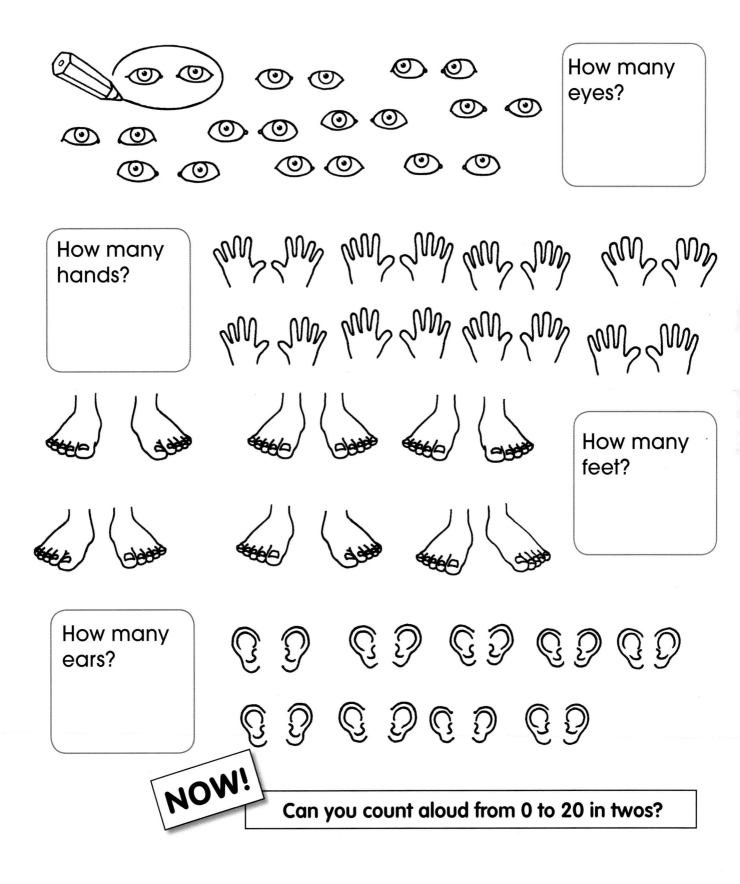

How many
eyes?

How many
hands?

How many
feet?

How many
ears?

NOW!

Can you count aloud from 0 to 20 in twos?

RE

- Read creation stories to the class from a variety of religions and cultures.
- Read a version of the Christian Garden of Eden story. Make a Garden of Eden model from a shallow tray filled with pebbles, sand, soil, plant cuttings, flower heads, water and model animals.
- Ask the children to collaborate on a large poster to illustrate the creation story, as shown here in the display.

PSHCE

- Discuss the importance of keeping our bodies clean. Compare the visual results when hands are washed in cold water, warm water and warm water with soap.
- Read *Dr Dog* by Babette Cole (Red Fox). Ask the children, '*What lifestyle advice would you give to the Gumboyle family?*'
- Invite the school nurse or school dentist into the class to talk about health and hygiene.
- Discuss safe places to play and road safety.
- Discuss 'stranger danger'.
- Ask the children to draw pictures of themselves taking care of their bodies, as shown on the activity sheet on page 13.

Ourselves

Keeping myself healthy and well

Draw a picture of yourself doing these things.

Keeping
my body clean

Drinking
water

Sleeping

TAKE GOOD
CARE OF
YOURSELF

Eating
healthy food

Taking
exercise

Think!

Do you do all five of these things every day?

Think of a different way of getting some exercise
for every day of the week.

Fantastic Photo Frames

Design & Technology

- Ask the children to design and make a photo frame for themselves, using a variety of real frames as a starting point for discussion of ideas. Decorate the frames and evaluate them against the original design. Identify what has worked well and suggest one improvement that could be made.

- Practise basic skills such as cutting, folding, hole punching and using split pins to create a moving model of themselves.

- Design and make a 'Special Memories' keepsake box. Ask the children to put items into the box that are special to them.

History

- Look at images of children from the past, for example from the Victorian era, and identify how aspects of their lives were different from our own. What clothes did children wear then? What were their toys like and how are they different to the toys of today?

- Make a toy museum in the classroom by asking parents and grandparents to loan items to you. Ask the children to put the toys into chronological order.

Geography

- Ask the children to draw or photograph their own home.

- Find the streets where the children live on an enlarged map of the local area. Plot where class members live on an enlarged map.

- Ask the children to draw a map of their route to school, including and labelling any local landmarks such as bridges, pubs, civic buildings and parks.

- Look at photos taken in the area and ask the children to place them in order, from the nearest to the furthest from the school.

- Use an online mapping resource such as Multimap to obtain a bird's-eye view of the streets that surround the school.

Ourselves

PE

- Explore the many different ways in which our bodies can move.

- Play the body parts game. Ask the children to travel around the hall space in a variety of ways, then call out a number of body parts such as 'six thumbs' or 'four knees'. The children must assemble themselves into groups that feature the correct number of the selected body part. Repeat by calling out other body parts.

Music

- Sing songs about the body such as *Heads, shoulders, knees and toes* (Anonymous) and *'I've got a body'* and *'He made me'* from *The complete come and praise* by Alison Carver et al. (BBC).

- Explore the sounds and effects that can be created using body parts percussion.

- Ask the children to gently place two fingers on their throat when speaking, singing or humming to feel the sound vibration created.

Art

- Look at self-portraits by famous or local artists. Invite a local artist into the classroom to talk about their work.

- Look at artists' works on a website such as the National Portrait Gallery (www.npg.org.uk). Use the zoomable pictures tool to examine artwork.

- Ask the children to use a mirror and draw a self-portrait using a variety of media. Draw portraits of class members. Make a class portrait gallery, as shown on the display.

- Create pictures using thumb prints.

- Create collaborative whole-class pictures using hands and footprints such as a rainbow, lion's mane or peacock's tail.

- Print close-up digital images of a face, then photocopy the image onto different colours of paper such as red, yellow, blue and green. Arrange the images together to form one large image.

Materials

These grids demonstrate the learning objectives covered in the activities within the theme. The curriculum references indicate the relevant programme of study (PoS) for a subject area unless otherwise stated.

	Learning Objectives	Curriculum References
Science (Page 18)		
Scientific Enquiry	Find out which materials are waterproof. Discuss a line of enquiry and plan how an idea may be tested. Make decisions about how to proceed.	Sc1/1;2a
	Make and discuss observations, recording these through drawing, writing and photography.	Sc1/2f,g; ICT PoS 3a
	Compare the actual results with the predicted. Draw and present conclusions.	Sc1/2i,j
Materials and Their Properties (QCA Science Unit 1C)	Handle a variety of materials. Name and describe the materials, their properties and their use.	Sc3/1a,c
	Choose and use a range of criteria to sort materials into groups. Identify why certain materials are used for a particular purpose.	Sc3/1b,d
Literacy (Page 20)		
Speaking and Listening	Read, re-tell and describe stories featuring materials.	En1/8a,b
	Use appropriate vocabulary and intonation when acting out stories to convey the feelings of story characters.	En1/1a,b
Drama	Perform a well known tale such as *The three little pigs* to others.	En1/1b;4a,b
Creating and Shaping Texts	Sequence events in well known stories and write suitable captions or speech bubbles.	En3/1f;2a
Engaging with and Responding to Texts	Read and re-tell traditional tales and compare different versions of the same story.	En2/6c
	Name significant characters, describe and explain their actions.	En2/3a
Mathematics (Page 22)		
Using and Applying Mathematics	Using the context of a building yard, solve one- and two-step word problems, choosing appropriate calculations. Explain methods. Show how a problem has been solved through drawing and number sentences.	Ma2/1c,i;4a
	Sort numbers into groups such as odd and even or by identifying multiples.	Ma2/2b
Understanding Shape	Name and describe the properties of 2-D and 3-D shapes found as objects of different materials.	Ma3/2b
Handling Data	Sort and organise shapes, numbers and information using charts, diagrams and results tables.	Ma2/5a

Learning Objectives	Curriculum References
History (Page 24)	
Discuss images and artefacts of different materials using appropriate historical vocabulary and sequence in chronological order.	PoS 1a,b
Compare materials in the past with the present day.	PoS 2b
Handle household artefacts and ask and answer questions about them.	PoS 4b; QCA History Unit 2
PE (Page 24)	
Use stories about building as a stimulus for creating and performing a sequence of actions and movements in a dance.	PoS 1b;2b;6a-d
Geography (Page 26)	
Through first-hand observation, investigate and identify the materials in the types of buildings, including housing, in the local streets.	PoS 1b,c;3a; QCA Geography Unit 1
Identify places in the local area that are changing and those that have remained the same for a period of time.	PoS 3c
Art (Page 26)	
Handle materials and discuss their shape, colour and texture.	PoS 4a; QCA Art Unit 1B
Investigate how materials have been used by different artists to create visual or tactile effects.	PoS 4c; QCA Art Unit 1C
Collect and sort materials according to their tactile or visual qualities.	PoS 2a;4a
Explore ways in which materials can be manipulated to create a range of effects.	PoS 2b
Music (Page 26)	
Identify the materials used in the manufacture of instruments and the resulting effect on the quality of sound produced.	PoS 4c
Explore the element of timbre by choosing and using instruments according to the nature of the sounds they produce.	PoS 2b
Sing songs and perform chants.	PoS 1a
Design & Technology (Page 27)	
Use first-hand observation, discussion and investigation to develop a design for a house.	PoS 1a-e;5a; QCA D&T Unit 1D
Experiment with construction techniques and ideas.	PoS 1b;2d
Follow a plan to create a house: assembling and joining component parts to produce a finished product.	PoS 2a-e
RE (Page 27)	
Read and re-tell stories featuring 'materials' from a variety of religions, discussing their meaning.	PoS 1a;2e;3f
Develop a sense of awe and wonder at the world in which we live.	PoS 2a
PSHCE (Page 27)	
Recognise the responsibilities that we have to recycle and re-use materials.	PoS 2a,b,g
Understand the need for positive choices and actions.	PoS 2c

Materials

Science

Starting Points

- Bring in a collection of natural and manufactured objects for the children to handle and discuss the material from which the items are made. Sort the objects into groups such as wood, metal, plastic, glass, clay and fabric. The items could also be sorted according to what they look or feel like, such as shiny, rough, bumpy, soft, smooth or hard, as shown in the display.

- Hold a materials hunt around the classroom or around the school. Why are objects made from certain materials and not others? Ask the children to hunt for materials around their own home. Cut out the pictures in the activity sheet on page 19 and sort them into groups based on their material.

Enquiry

- Discuss the desirability of a waterproof roof. Ask the children to predict which materials may be best for this purpose. Arrange the children in small mixed-ability teams and provide each team with a roofless 'house' made from wooden bricks or a construction kit.

- Place a small toy inside the 'house' and provide teams with a selection of materials, such as aluminium foil, plastic from a carrier bag, woven fabric such as hessian, paper towel, kitchen roll, wooden lolly sticks and hay with which to construct a roof. The children should be asked to discuss and predict which material will make the most waterproof roof and so keep the toy the driest. Children could rank the materials from best to worst before the test. Explain to the children that they must each use material to create a roof for their house and then test each one for its waterproof quality.

- Provide each group with a plastic beaker of water and a pipette and introduce the notion of a fair test by instructing that in each instance the same number of drops of water must be applied to each house. Provide the children with a recording grid for the results. When all of the materials have been tested, each team should feed back their results to the whole class. Find out how the materials were ranked. Were the results from each group similar? Which material came out on top? Which material was the worst at keeping the toy dry? Did anything unexpected happen? Encourage the children to explain their results to others.

Extension Activities

- Examine the materials used in the 'roof' experiment using a digital microscope linked to an interactive white board. Capture and print images of the materials and add these to the children's written recordings. Can the children link the structure of the material, revealed by the microscope, to what happened in the test?

Materials in my home

Here are some things found in and around a house. Cut out the pictures and sort them into groups according to the materials from which they are made.

plastic	wood
glass	metal

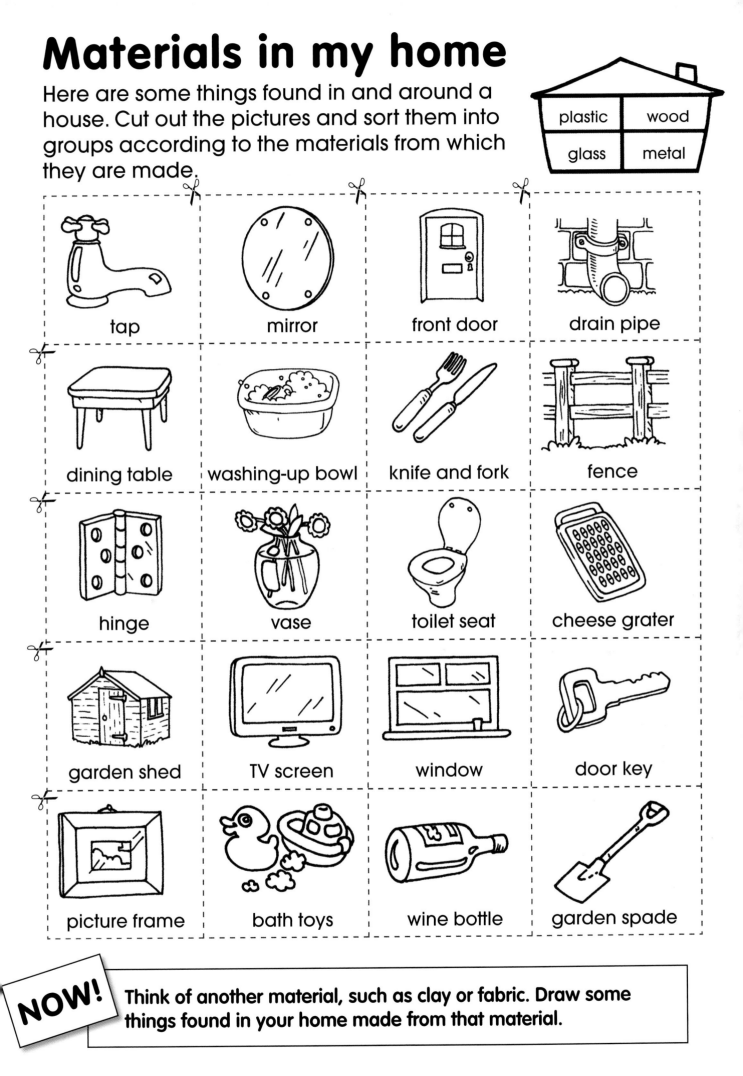

tap	mirror	front door	drain pipe
dining table	washing-up bowl	knife and fork	fence
hinge	vase	toilet seat	cheese grater
garden shed	TV screen	window	door key
picture frame	bath toys	wine bottle	garden spade

NOW! Think of another material, such as clay or fabric. Draw some things found in your home made from that material.

Literacy

Speaking and Listening

● Ask the children to write a play script based on the story of *The three little pigs*. Make masks or simple puppets using wooden spoons and fabric and use these to perform the story to others, using the children's own scripts.

● Use a video camera to record a dramatic performance of the story.

● Ask children to pretend to be the wolf. Interview the 'wolf', ensuring that the children answer the questions in character.

Reading and Writing

● Read *Another fine mess* by Tony Bonning (Gullane) and suggest ideas for how the animals are going to re-use and recycle the different materials at the end of the story.

● Ask the children to write labels to accompany a picture taken from the end of the *Another fine mess* story. Stick the labels to the picture, as illustrated in the display photograph.

● Read and re-tell *The house that Jack built* by Jeanette Winter (Picture Puffins).

● Read *The three little pigs* illustrated by Jan Lewis (Ladybird). Compare different versions of the story, why do these variations occur? Ask the children to re-tell the story.

● Provide the children with pictures of *The three little pigs* story to be sequenced in the correct order. Using the pictures as a writing frame, ask the children to write captions for each picture.

● Ask the children to imagine what each pig might say about his house and the materials he has used. Ask the children to write text in the form of speech bubbles for the characters in the story, as shown in the activity sheet on page 21.

● Use a word processor to write factual information about the properties of different materials using a word bank and insert pictures into the text.

Materials

Even numbers always end in 2, 4, 6, 8 or 0.

Odd numbers always end in 1, 3, 5, 7 or 9.

Maths

Using and Applying

- Using the context of the cost of different materials in a builder's yard, ask the children to solve one- and two-step word problems involving money using amounts up to 20 pence, 50 pence or one pound.

- Using the context of houses, explore the pattern of odd and even house numbers, such as those in Evens Street and Odds Avenue, as shown in the display. Ask the children to sort numbers into odd or even, as shown on the activity sheet on page 23.

Understanding Shape

- Ask the children to sort materials according to a variety of criteria using large sorting hoops or a grid shown on an interactive whiteboard.

- Construct a Venn diagram using overlapping sorting hoops and sort materials or objects according to chosen characteristics.

Handling Data

- Name and describe the 2-D and 3-D shapes of items used inside and outside a house, for example ceramic bathroom tiles, plastic pipes, bricks.

- Create a tally chart of the shapes. Construct a sorting diagram or table with the information collected.

- Examine, create and continue the pattern used by builders when constructing a wall from bricks. Explore how other shapes can tessellate.

Materials

Odd and even numbers

Look at the numbers. If they are odd, circle them with a green colour, if they are even circle them with a red colour.

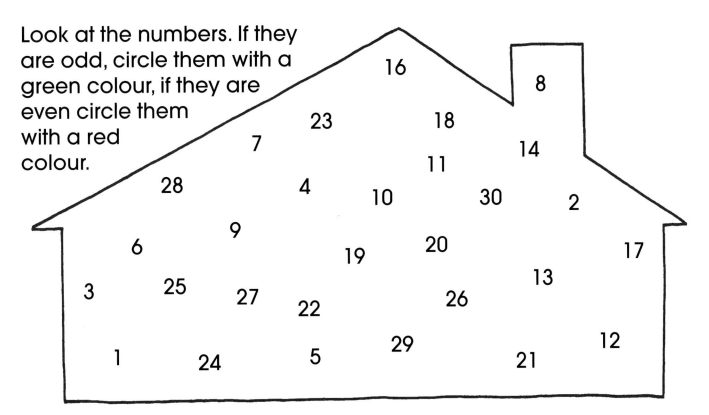

16 8 23 18 7 14 11 28 4 10 30 2 9 6 19 20 17 3 25 27 22 26 13 1 24 5 29 21 12

Now sort out the numbers into these two groups.
Write the numbers in the correct house.

Less than 15

More than 15

NOW!

What number is your house? Is it odd or even?

History

- Compare the materials used in the construction of houses and other buildings today and in the past. Suggest reasons for the differences that occur. Observe and record the materials that have been used in the construction of buildings in your local area. Compare a Victorian house with a recent housing development.

- Ask whether the materials used in houses and other buildings give us a clue to the age of a house, for example a timber-framed house, a thatched roof, a flint wall. Place images of buildings in chronological order.

- Compare the use of different materials used to create household objects and toys in the past and in the present day. Use the activity sheet on page 25 to compare household objects.

- Compare the use of materials in specific rooms in the house in the past and present day, for example in old and new bathrooms as shown in the display.

PE

- Using the story of *The house that Jack built* re-told by Jeanette Winter (Picture Puffins) as a stimulus, rehearse elements of a 'work dance', exploring actions such as sawing, chopping, hammering or sanding.

- Create a 'work dance' by sequencing these actions and perform to another class.

Children had a bath once a week. A tin bath was put in front of the fire and water was poured in using a jug.

100 years ago there was no electricity. So they lit fires to keep them warm and used candles to help them see.

In the house
Now and then

Look at these household items from the past and the present day. What are they made from? Write in the missing words.

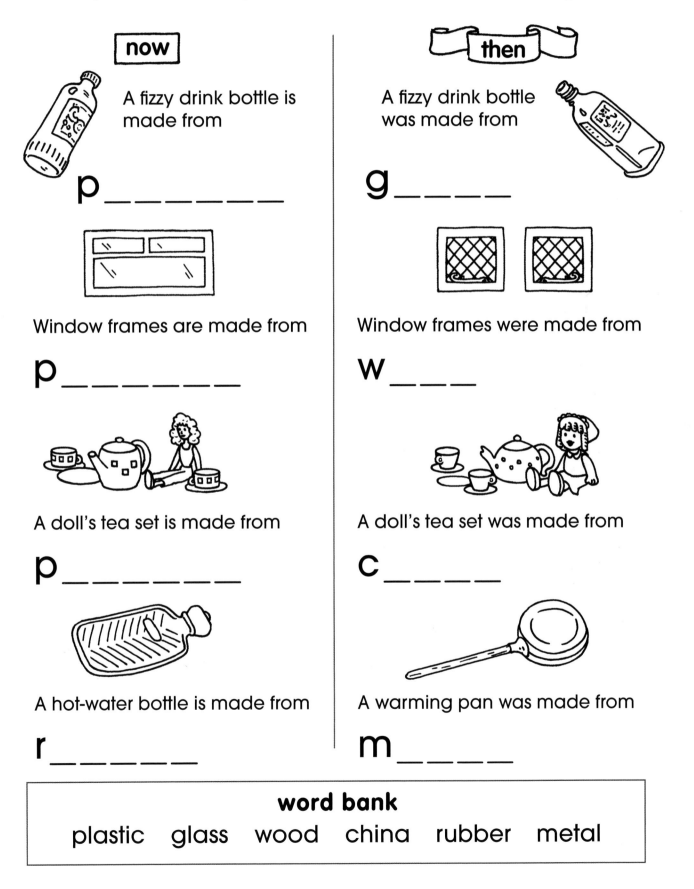

now

A fizzy drink bottle is made from

p _ _ _ _ _ _ _

Window frames are made from

p _ _ _ _ _ _ _

A doll's tea set is made from

p _ _ _ _ _ _ _

A hot-water bottle is made from

r _ _ _ _ _ _

then

A fizzy drink bottle was made from

g _ _ _ _ _

Window frames were made from

w _ _ _ _

A doll's tea set was made from

c _ _ _ _ _

A warming pan was made from

m _ _ _ _ _

word bank
plastic   glass   wood   china   rubber   metal

•   Materials   •   Belair Curricular-Links Science 1

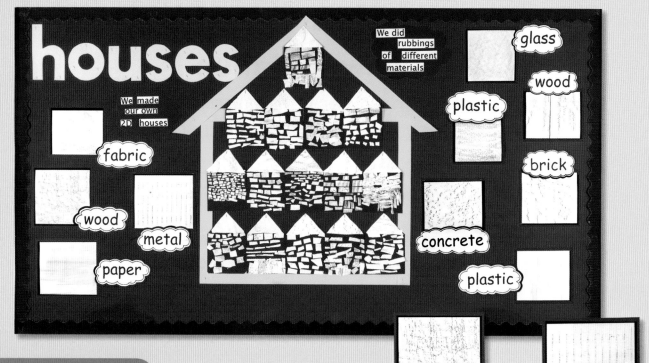

Geography

- Identify which naturally occurring materials are found in the local area such as a slate quarry, chalk cliff, metal ore mine or a gravel pit. Locate these places on a map of the area. Discuss how locally available materials been used in the local environment, for example, slate being used to create roof tiles, clay being used to create pottery.

- Observe and record the materials that have been used in the construction of buildings in the immediate vicinity around the school.

- If possible, visit an area that is undergoing change, such as a new housing development or the construction of a new school. Why is the change happening? What is the response amongst local people to the change? Which materials are being used in the construction?

- Read *Homes around the world* by Margaret C. Hall (Heinemann Educational) and compare the materials used in homes and houses around the world.

Art

- Observe and draw houses and other buildings in the local area.

- Using thin paper and wax crayon, make rubbings of different materials that have been used around the school such as a rubbing of a metal drain cover or a rubbing of the wood grain in a fence. Illustrate the patterns that different materials make, as shown here in the display photograph.

- Explore the effects that can be created by cutting, folding, snipping, fringing, scrunching, rolling and twisting different kinds of paper. Use bright coloured paper and display the results on a black background.

- Make a collage from natural materials such as twigs, leaves and seeds.

- Make a collage from manufactured materials such as plastic packaging.

- Look at the work of contemporary sculptors such as Anthony Gormley (b. 1950) and Andrew Goldsworthy (b. 1956).

- Discuss the materials used and the effects created.

- Make a large, collaborative temporary sculpture from natural materials, for example, create a sculpture on the classroom floor of a person using leaves or outside on the playground using wooden blocks or timber offcuts.

- Make smaller, individual sculptures from materials such as pebbles, plastic buttons or cardboard tubes.

Materials

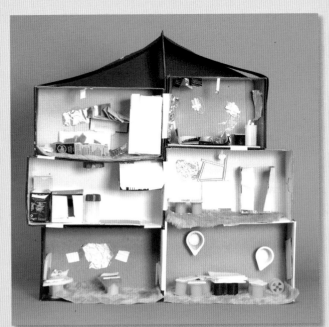

Music

- Look at and handle a collection of musical instruments and sort them into groups according to which materials they have been made from.

- Explore the quality of sound that different materials make, such as comparing the sound created when striking a wooden xylophone with the metallic sound of a glockenspiel.

- Perform a chant using *The house that Jack built* by Jeanette Winter (Picture Puffins) as a starting point.

Design & Technology

- Use a variety of construction kits to create buildings, include specific features such as doors or a pitched roof. Compare different kits and ask the children to rank them in terms of enjoyment in their use. Contact the manufacturer with the results. Do the children prefer to use wooden, plastic or metal kits?

- Look at a doll's house and identify the different materials used in its construction. Ask the children to design a room for a doll's house, using images from magazines, samples of paint colours, pieces of wallpaper and fabric swatches to create a 'mood board' for the room. Using the design ideas and mood board, create a room, using a shoebox as the initial 'shell'. Attach four or six finished rooms together to create a collaborative doll's house. Use a digital camera to photograph the final product.

RE

- Read and discuss stories from a variety of religions and cultures that feature obvious use of materials, for example the Christian story of *The foolish person who built his house on sand,* as shown here in the display.

PSHCE

- Discuss what happens to rubbish and waste materials. Invite the recycling officer from the local council to come and talk to the children about waste management and recycling initiatives in your local area.

- Show the children a selection of household rubbish. Identify what the items have been made from and which can be recycled.

- Ask the children if they recycle any of their household waste. Design and make posters or leaflets to encourage more families to recycle.

Growing Plants

These grids demonstrate the learning objectives covered in the activities within the theme. The curriculum references indicate the relevant programme of study (PoS) for a subject area unless otherwise stated.

	Learning Objectives	Curriculum References
Science (Page 30)		
Scientific Enquiry	Pose and answer questions about plants through observation, measurement and obtaining evidence.	Sc1/1;2a
	Use close observation and first-hand experiences.	Sc1/2b
	Record and share findings.	Sc1/2f,g; ICT PoS 2a;3a
	Consider and compare evidence.	Sc1/2h,i
Life Processes and Living Things (QCA Science Unit 1B)	Understand that plants require water and light in order to grow.	Sc2/3a
	Name parts of plants.	Sc2/3b
	Understand that seeds grow into plants.	Sc2/3c
Literacy (Page 32)		
Speaking and Listening	Re-tell a well known story featuring plants, such as *Jack and the beanstalk*.	En1/1b,d;8a
Drama	Act out stories.	En1/4b/11b
	Interact with others through a role play garden centre setting.	En1/4a
Listening and Responding	Listen to a gardener and ask questions.	En1/2a,e
Engaging with and Responding to Texts	Select and read books with a plant theme, talk about their choices.	En2/3c
Creating and Shaping Texts	Write a new ending for a well known story.	En3/1f
	Write your own 'traditional' story.	En3/1f;2d
	Create a plant diary.	En3/1d;9a
Mathematics (Page 34)		
Counting and Understanding Number	Count small objects such as seeds and use ways to organise counting.	Ma2/1d;2a
	Use estimation of number.	Ma2/1i; Ma3/4c
Using and Applying Mathematics	Create and describe repeating patterns using leaf rubbings.	Ma2/2b
Measuring	Use time-related vocabulary.	Ma3/1d;4a
	Sequence months and seasons.	Ma3/4a
	Measure leaves and plants.	Ma3/4a,c
Handling Data	Sort leaves into groups.	Ma2/1g;5a
	Collect and record information about plants.	Ma2/5a; ICT PoS 1a
	Present information in the form of a table or graph.	Ma2/5a; ICT PoS 3a

Learning Objectives	Curriculum References
Geography (Page 36)	
Make observations about plants and record information.	PoS 1b;4a
Record location of plants on a map of the school.	PoS 2c
History (Page 36)	
Compare gardening tools and methods from different times; identify differences.	PoS 2b
Ask questions about the passage of time and changes in plants such as trees.	PoS 4b
RE (Page 36)	
Identify and compare festivals and celebrations linked to food.	PoS 1b
Design & Technology (Page 38)	
Design and make products, using a variety of starting points.	PoS 2d;5c
Evaluate commercially available gifts.	PoS 5a
Try out garden design ideas on-screen.	PoS 1b; ICT PoS 2a
Music (Page 38)	
Sing and perform songs and rhymes about plants and growth.	PoS 1a,c
Compose music in a collaborative group.	PoS 2a,b;3b
PE (Page 38)	
Use a story about a seed growing as a starting point for dance.	PoS 6a
Create and perform dance steps and sequences.	PoS 6c,d
Art (Page 39)	
Use a range of techniques to depict plants including printing and sewing.	PoS 2b;4a
Produce models of flowers and vegetables.	PoS 5b
Work with others to create a plant wall hanging.	PoS 5b
PSHCE (Page 39)	
Understand how to make healthy choices when eating.	PoS 3a
Contribute to a school garden project.	PoS 2h
Look after livings things such as plants.	PoS 2e

Growing Plants

Science

Starting Points

● Look at and talk about a variety of seeds. Soak some large seeds, such as broad beans, until the outer skin is easy to peel off. Split open the seed and look at the embryonic shoot. You could use a digital microscope or a hand lens to get a close-up look.

● Remove a pot plant from its pot to examine its roots. Grow a bulb in a transparent container to watch the roots form and grow.

● Ask the children to talk about the things a seed or plant needs in order for it to grow. Ask them to think of a way that their ideas could be tested.

Enquiry

● Choose four healthy, identical bedding plants. Explain to the children that they are going to find out what happens when a plant is denied light, water or both. Explain that one of the four plants will be given both light and water. One of the plants will be allowed light, but is not to be watered. Position these two plants side by side. One of the plants is to be put in a dark place such as a cupboard, but is still to be watered and finally one plant will be placed in the same dark place but will not be watered. Use a measuring jug to measure out the water and talk about how it is important to keep this amount the same for all of the plants that are watered. Encourage the children to predict what will happen to each plant. Ask the children to draw the four plants on the activity sheet on page 31.

● Check on the plants once a week over a period of four weeks. Each time the plants are checked, encourage the children to look carefully at the plants, making notes or drawings of the things that they observe. Keep a photographic record using a digital camera.

● At the end of four weeks, re-examine all of the plants and talk about what has happened to them. Is this what the children expected? What have they found out about growing plants?

Extension Activities

● Many plants are grown for food. Can the children identify which part of a plant certain foodstuffs have come from? Show the children a selection of foods such as cabbage, carrots, celery, lettuce, sweetcorn, rice, apples, rhubarb, parsnip, pears or beans. Ask the children to identify the items then to sort them according to which part of the plant they think the food has come from. For instance, roots, leaves, seeds, stems or fruits.

● Ask the children to describe herbs using their senses of sight, smell and taste, as shown in the display.

Growing plants

Choose four identical, healthy plants. For two weeks provide one plant with light and water. Provide one plant with light only. Provide one plant with water only and one plant with neither light nor water. After two weeks, draw what each plant looks like in the boxes below.

☀ light	✓	◌ water	✓

☀ light	✓	◌ water	✗

☀ light	✗	◌ water	✓

☀ light	✗	◌ water	✗

NOW! What do the results tell you about growing plants? Talk to a friend about what has happened.

Literacy

Speaking and Listening

● Make some simple props such as masks and act a story, for example *The enormous turnip* by Irene Yates (Ladybird).

● Create a garden centre in your role play area. Ask the children to create and display adverts for the garden centre and to produce labels for the products on sale.

● Find out if there is a gardening club or an allotment society in your local area. Invite a gardener in to give a demonstration and to speak to the class.

Reading and Writing

● Read non-fiction texts such as *Find out about plants* by Steven Pollock (BBC) and *My bean diary* by Rhonda Jenkins (Heinemann).

● Read the traditional story *Jack and the beanstalk* (Ladybird Books). Ask the children to re-tell the story, using some of the vocabulary contained in the story. Then compare the tale to a different version of the story such as *Jim and the beanstalk* by Raymond Briggs (Penguin Books).

● Write an alternative ending for the *Jack and the beanstalk* story.

● Ask the children to write their own story about some magic beans or seeds that grow into something quite unexpected!

● Make a class collection of stories that feature plants such as *Jack and the beanstalk* (Ladybird Books), *The enormous turnip* by Irene Yates (Ladybird) or *The trouble with grandad* by Babette Cole (Atria Books). Encourage the children to read and talk about the stories together, making recommendations to others.

● Grow some runner or broad beans and write a daily 'bean diary' to keep account of the growth that takes place.

● Write simple sentences to accompany the pictures for the activity sheet on page 33.

● Take photographs using a digital camera of children planting seeds or bulbs, then ask them to write simple captions for each picture, as illustrated here on the display.

● On shaped paper, for instance leaf shapes, display a collection of plant-related words. You could display your leaves on a 'beanstalk' growing around the walls and ceiling.

Growing Plants

growing plants

Cut out these pictures. Put them in the correct order then write a caption for each one.

seeds

Remember to put a full stop at the end!

NOW!

Draw and label a picture of what your plant will look like when it has grown.

Don't forget to use a capital letter at the beginning of each sentence!

Maths

Understanding Number

● Fill a large, transparent jar with sunflower seeds or beans. Ask the children to estimate how many seeds or beans the jar contains. Let the children record their estimates on poster paper left next to the jar and provide a prize for the closest estimate. This approach should discourage the children from making wild guesses! Tip out the beans or seeds and count them.

Measuring

● Grow a fast-growing plant such as an amaryllis or some runner beans. Take daily measurements of the plant's growth, as illustrated on the display and on the activity sheet on page 35, and record these on a chart or grid. Use the data to produce a line graph.

● Ask the children to think of a way to measure the outer edge of a large leaf, such as a cabbage leaf, where clearly a ruler is not the best option.

● Link the growing seasons of plants with work on time. Ask the children to place the four seasons in correct sequence or arrange the months of the year correctly. Use picture clues such as planting bulbs in the autumn, apple blossom in the spring and wheat ripening in the summer to assist the sequencing procedure.

Handling Data

● Use sorting hoops to sort leaves into groups. Provide criteria for sorting such as green/not green, hairy/smooth, large/small, edible/not edible, then encourage the children to think of their own ways to sort the leaves. Then overlap the two sorting hoops to create a Venn diagram for sorting.

Using and Applying

● Make repeating patterns, using real leaves, rubbings of leaves or printed pictures.

● Ask the children to solve a word problem, such as that illustrated in the display.

Growing Plants

Measuring

Use a ruler to measure the height of these flowers. Write the height in centimetres.

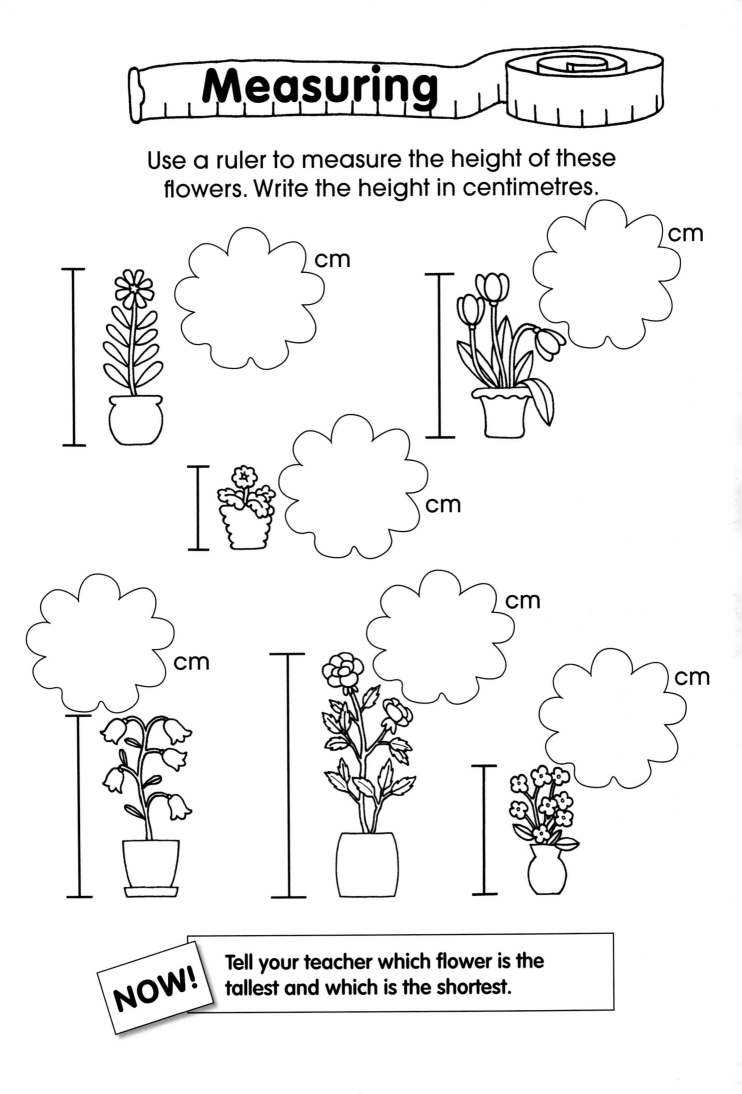

NOW! Tell your teacher which flower is the tallest and which is the shortest.

On the terrace: forget-me-not, buddleia, lavender

On the playground: holm oak, moss

On the bank: grass, shepherd's purse, daisy

By the gate: buttercup, dandelion, clover

plants

daisy

Geography

- Go on a plant hunt around the school grounds. Use the activity sheet on page 37 to narrow the search to specific plants. Keep a note of the location in which the plants were found. Look at an enlarged map of the school grounds. Ask the children to use the map to identify where plants were found and to write their findings on the activity sheet.

- Attach photographs or pictures of the plants to a display board to show where the plants were found.

- Look on a map of the local area and talk about the places in the locality where plants can be found, such as the local park or public gardens, allotments or cultivated land.

- Show the children a collection of fruits and vegetables. Ask them to decide whether the products have been grown in the UK or have been grown and then imported from other countries. Once the vegetables have been sorted in this manner, reveal the country of origin to the children. Find the countries on a globe or in an atlas. Talk about our climate and which products grow well here. Compare our climate with that of other places that favour the growth of other foodstuffs.

History

- Allow the children to look at and carefully handle a selection of old and new gardening tools. Ask them to describe the tactile qualities of the tools and the materials used in their manufacture. This might include looking at an old trowel made from metal with a wooden handle against a modern trowel moulded from a single piece of plastic, or an old galvanised metal watering can compared to a modern green plastic item. Ask the children to sort the tools into 'old' and 'new' groups and ask them to give reasons for their choices.

⚠ Safety note: check that all tools are safe to handle!

- Discuss the longevity of trees.

RE

- Look at celebrations and festivals linked to the notion of giving thanks for food.
- Talk about what Christians do to celebrate harvest. Focus the discussion on the school harvest festival.
- Compare a Christian harvest festival to the Jewish festival of Sukkot.

Looking for plants

Go on a plant hunt around your school grounds.
Keep a note of which plants you find and their location.

moss	daisy	ivy
I found this by the…	I found this on the…	I found this on the…
dandelion	**clover**	**plantain**
I found this by the…	I found this by the…	I found this on the…
bindweed	**bramble**	**nettle**
I found this on the…	I found this near the…	I found this by the…

NOW! Cut out the plant pictures and stick them onto a map of the school to show where they were found.

a gift for gardeners

a fork

seeds

Broad Bean

gardening gloves

a sun hat

bubble bath

SOOTHING BATH FOAM

a kneeling mat

We have designed a gift basket for a gardener.

What do you think a gardener would like?

a trowel

Design & Technology

- Look at some commercially available gift products targeted at gardeners. From this starting point, ask the children to think of items that gardeners would like to receive as a gift.

- Show the children a trug or woven basket and challenge them to design a gift for a gardener, filling the trug with appropriate items, as illustrated here on the display. Encourage the children to talk about their ideas then draw and label the items that they would choose.

- Design and make food products from plants, ideally including plants that have been grown by the children themselves. This might include a herby salad dressing, using fresh herbs grown by the children, or a green salad using home-grown lettuce or onions.

- Design and make a scarecrow for your school vegetable patch. Hold a best-dressed scarecrow competition.

- Design a scarer to stop Peter Rabbit from eating all the vegetables in Mr MacGregor's garden as in *The tale of Peter Rabbit* by Beatrix Potter (Penguin Putnam). Look at a football supporters 'rattle' as a starting point.

- Design a garden online in the kid's activity section at www.geffrye-museum.org.uk.

a fork

Music

- Learn to sing the song 'Paintbox' (commonly known as the 'Cauliflowers fluffy' song) in *Harlequin* by David Gadsby and Beatrice Harrop (published by A & C Black). Perform the song to another class or as part of a celebration such as harvest.

- Sing the traditional nursery rhyme *Mary, Mary, quite contrary*. Ask the children to compose their own nursery rhyme about growing plants to the same tune.

a trowel

- Sing the hand rhyme *One potato, two potato*. The children could make up their own rhymes about other vegetables with actions.

- Ask the children to use percussion instruments to experiment with sound effects that might be suitable to suggest the growth of plants. Compose a short piece of music using these ideas. The music could be intended to represent a flower bud unfurling or a seed sprouting a shoot through the soil and into the daylight.

PE

- Use a story such as *The tiny seed* by Eric Carle (Picture Puffins) as the structure for a dance. The children should suggest different actions for each section of the seed's growth.

- Practise dance steps then sequence into a routine to perform a group 'Happy harvest' barn dance.

Art

- Decorate a plain clay plant pot with bright painted designs.

- Look at the work of artists who use flowers and plants as their subject matter. For instance, show the children some work by Georgia O'Keeffe (1887–1986) and ask them to talk about the paintings. Ask the children to produce their own paintings in a similar style to Georgia O'Keeffe's, using strong, bold designs. Pin the children's art work to a large sheet and display the collection of images. View images of plants by Georgia O'Keeffe online at a website such as www.essentialart.com.

- Ask each child to create a sewn patch, featuring a flower or leaf, to contribute to a whole-class fabric wall hanging, such as that shown here. Children could use stitching or beads to embellish their item.

- Create 3-D models of flowers, fruits and vegetables using modelling clay or papier mâché.

- Look at how plants, flowers, fruit and vegetables have been used to create decorative displays in churches for harvest festivals. Use a selection of items to create your own decorative tabletop display.

PSHCE

- Establish a school gardening club. Encourage children to be responsible for the care and maintenance of the plants. Grow a variety of plants, encompassing attractive flowers, along with fruit and vegetables that can be picked and eaten by those involved in their growth.

- Talk about the need to eat fruit and vegetables as part of a healthy diet.

- Hold a tasting session of some unusual fruits that the children may not have tried before such as papaya or passion fruit.

Sound & Hearing

These grids demonstrate the learning objectives covered in the activities within the theme. The curriculum references indicate the relevant programme of study (PoS) for a subject area unless otherwise stated.

	Learning Objectives	Curriculum References
Science (Page 42)		
Scientific Enquiry	Plan and carry out an investigation about distance and sound, predicting what might happen.	Sc1/2b,c
	Make observations and record measurements.	Sc1/2f
	Draw conclusions and explain them to others.	Sc1/1;2i
Physical Processes (QCA Science Unit 1F)	Identify different types of sound and sound sources.	Sc4/3c
	Find information about animals' ears on a CD-ROM or website.	Sc2/2a; ICT PoS 1a
	Understand that sounds travel away from their source, becoming fainter the further they travel.	Sc4/3d
	Recognise that the outer ear is shaped to catch and funnel sounds and that sounds are heard when they enter the ear.	Sc4/3c,d
Literacy (Page 44)		
Listening and Responding	Convey messages by whispering.	En1/1f
	Play listening games.	En1/2a,b
	Respond to sound patterns such as rhyme.	En1/2f
	Listen to and identify mystery sound effects.	En1/2a
	Use equipment to record and play back sounds.	ICT PoS 1b,c
	Explore sound effects software.	ICT PoS 5b
Understanding and Interpreting Texts	Read fiction and identify main events.	En2/3a,b
Engaging with and Responding to Texts	Read non-fiction texts about sound, read for information gathering.	En2/2a
Creating and Shaping Texts	Discuss, collect and display topic words about sound and hearing.	En2/1j
	Use stories as a model for own writing.	En3/1f
	Write labels and captions about sound for pictures.	En3/1c
	Collect words about sound and use as a basis for a poem.	En3/2a
	Write instructions for making a musical instrument.	En3/9a,d
Mathematics (Page 46)		
Counting and Understanding Number	Explore addition patterns related to making ten.	Ma2/2b
Measuring	Choose and use appropriate measuring equipment for a sound investigation.	Ma3/4a
	Use the language of measurement correctly.	Ma3/1d
	Measure distances and objects.	Ma3/4a
	Sort items by size using estimation and comparison.	Ma3/1b-d;4a,c
Handling Data	Use images, tables and charts to sort, organise and present information about instruments.	Ma2/5a,b; ICT PoS 5b

Learning Objectives	Curriculum References
Music (Page 48)	
Play instruments with and to others.	PoS 1b,c
Explore the various qualities of sound.	PoS 2b
Investigate how sounds can be made.	PoS 4c
Compose and create music.	PoS 2a
Use graphic notation.	PoS 4c
Listen to and identify sounds.	PoS 4a
Listen to recorded music.	PoS 5d
PE (Page 48)	
Apply skills collaboratively with a partner.	PoS 2a
Observe and describe the work of others.	PoS 3b
Design & Technology (Page 50)	
Appraise a range of instruments.	PoS 5a
Discuss and sketch ideas for making an instrument.	PoS 1a,c,e
Follow a design brief to create a simple musical instrument.	PoS 2a,d
Decorate the finished instrument, evaluate success against the design intention.	PoS 2e,3b
Art (Page 50)	
Produce images in response to music stimuli.	PoS 1a;2c;5a
Look at work featuring instruments produced by a variety of artists.	PoS 4c
Draw ears from close observation.	PoS 1a
Explore imaginative collage ideas using one repeated image.	PoS 5a,c
Geography (Page 51)	
Locate countries on a map or a globe.	PoS 2c
Gather information about musical instruments in these countries from first-hand experiences and secondary sources.	PoS 1a;2d
History (Page 51)	
Find out about the work of a famous scientist such as Thomas Edison.	PoS 6c
Gather information from a variety of sources.	PoS 4a
PSHCE (Page 51)	
Name parts of the body.	PoS 3e
Discuss hearing loss and deafness.	PoS 4c
Identify activities that may be hazardous to our sense of hearing.	PoS 3a
Identify ways to protect our ears.	PoS 3g

Sound & Hearing

Science

Starting Points

- Ask the children to talk about sounds that they like and dislike.

- Go on a 'listening walk' around the school and record by drawing the things that were heard. This could be the basis for a display.

- Introduce the idea of sound as a vibration. Ask the children to watch a triangle or tuning fork vibrate as it is struck. A vibrating tuning fork may also be placed in a container of water to produce a splash!

- Ask the children to hold an inflated balloon next to a speaker when music is playing and describe what they can feel, or to place their fingers gently against their throat when they are speaking or humming.

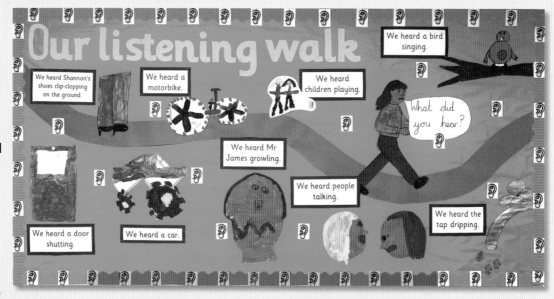

Enquiry

- Reiterate the notion that sounds start off as vibrations and travel through the air as sound waves. Explain that the shape of our ears funnels the sound waves into our ears.

- Introduce a travelling sounds investigation, stating that the children will be investigating the distance travelled by a sound wave and whether or not a larger 'ear', using a cone of card, can enable us to hear sounds from further away. Show the children the sound sources that are going to be tested such as a ticking clock and a mobile phone. The children might like to make a verbal prediction about which object it will be possible to hear from the furthest away and which object may only be heard at close range. They might also like to comment about the possible effect of using an ear cone.

- Measure out a length of the playground using metre sticks. Test one sound source at a time, asking a volunteer to be blindfolded then walk slowly forwards, towards the source of the sound, raising their hand when they can hear the sound. This distance should be recorded on the activity sheet on page 43. Work through a variety of sound sources. Then repeat the investigation, but this time ask the volunteer to use an ear cone, made from a sheet of card, held up to their ear. Record the results as before.

- Discuss the results and whether they were as expected. Discuss what has been learnt through the investigation and whether this information could have a practical use. Perhaps the investigation could be repeated at a busy, noisy time such as during playtime. What effect might this have on the results?

Extension Activities

- Ask the children if they have heard of the expression of being able to hear a 'pin drop'. Try this out in the classroom or in a whole school assembly. If a pin is dropped onto the floor, is it possible to hear it land and if so, from how far away?

- Can sound travel through water? Can sound travel through a solid wall? Ask the children to suggest a way to investigate these hypotheses.

Travelling sounds

How good are your ears at hearing sounds? Try this test in the playground. Blindfold a friend. Approach them with a sound source, using metre sticks to measure the distance away, beginning at a distance of 20 metres. Ask your friend to raise their hand when they hear the sound. Write down how many metres away they are standing. Repeat the investigation but this time provide your friend with an ear cone made from a sheet of card.

Sound source tested:	I heard the sound from this far away **without** an ear cone:	I heard the sound from this far away **with** an ear cone:
Ticking alarm clock		
Radio on low volume		
Mobile phone ringtone on low setting		
Talking doll or toy		
Pouring dry sand from one container to another		

NOW! Talk about your results. Were you able to hear sounds better with or without the ear cone? Why do you think this might be?

Literacy

Speaking and Listening

- Sit everyone in a large circle and play a game of Chinese whispers.

- Use a microphone to record sounds. Create a sound effects tape to play to other children who must try to identify the sound source.

Reading and Writing

- Read the book *Have you got my purr?* by Judy West and Tim Warnes (Little Tiger Press). Talk about the different animal sounds in the story. The storyline of the kitten who has lost its purr is illustrated in the display photograph here.

- Use the format of the *Have you got my purr?* story as a framework for writing a similar story, perhaps featuring a talking musical instrument, which has become lost in an orchestra.

- Read *The surprise party* by Pat Hutchins (Macmillan). Talk about how the message about the party became muddled in the story and what happened as a result. How was the crisis resolved? Ask the children to refer back to the text when answering such questions.

- Write a non-chronological report about school sounds, having been on a listening walk around the school.

- Talk about and write a list of favourite sounds. This could then become the basis for a poem, such as shown on the activity sheet on page 45.

- Write step by step instructions as to how to make a stringed musical instrument, such as those shown on page 50.

- Ask the children to produce labels for a classroom display on sound vibrations.

Sound & Hearing

A world of sound

Read the first verse of this poem.
Can you spot the pattern of rhyming words?
The second and the fourth lines rhyme.

Use this pattern to complete the second and third verses with your own ideas.

I love the sound of singing birds,

I love the swash of the sea.

I love the sound of clapping hands,

It's a world of sound for me.

I love the sound of _____.

I love the buzz of a bee.

I love the sound of _____.

It's a world of sound for me.

I love the sound of _____.

I love the _____.

I love the sound of _____.

It's a world of sound for me!

NOW! Make up your own poem about the sounds that you don't like to hear. Talk about these sounds first, to start you off.

number bonds to 10

6 + 4 = 10

7 + 3 = 10

10 + 0 = 10

5 + 5 = 10

8 + 2 = 10

9 + 1 = 10

Maths

Measuring

- Use metre sticks to measure out the playground for the travelling sounds investigation on page 43. Then record results in metres and centimetres from the travelling sounds investigation.

- Use a ruler or tape measure to measure the size of an ear. Sort classroom objects into groups, smaller than and larger than the size of a human ear, as on the activity sheet on page 47.

- Ask the children to estimate, discuss and order by comparison a series of animal ears, from smallest to largest.

6 + 4 = 10

Handling Data

- Ask the children to use a digital camera to take photos of musical instruments. These could be used in a sorting activity, using large hoops placed on the floor. Sort using a variety of 'sound' criteria. For example 'instruments that are plucked' or 'instruments that are hit'.

- Present the results from the Travelling sounds activity sheet on page 43 in the form of a table or graph.

Understanding Number

- Create a display showing the number bands to 10 using cut-out paper tambourines.

- Ribbon or strips of paper can be used on the display to link the tambourines that make ten. If the display is at child height, the children can do this task for themselves.

9 + 1 = 10

Sound & Hearing

Ears in order!

Talk about these animal ears with a friend. Cut out the pictures of ears. Sort and stick them in size order, from SMALLEST to LARGEST. Think about the size of the animal to help you.

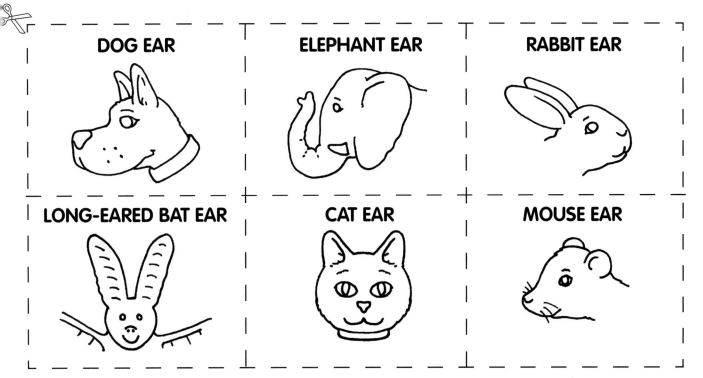

MEASURE AND COMPARE!

Find five things in the classroom SMALLER than your ear.
Draw them here:

Measure the length of your ear with a ruler.

Find five things in the classroom LARGER than your ear.
Draw them here:

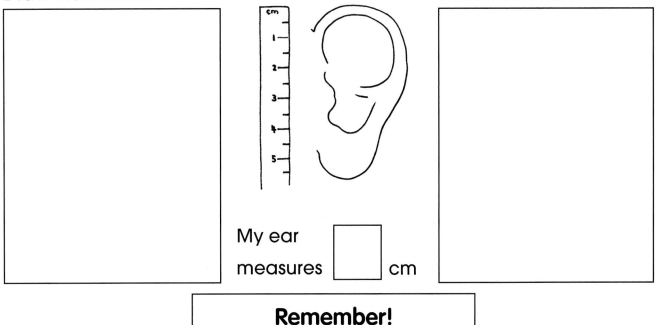

My ear measures ☐ cm

Remember!
NEVER insert objects into your ear.

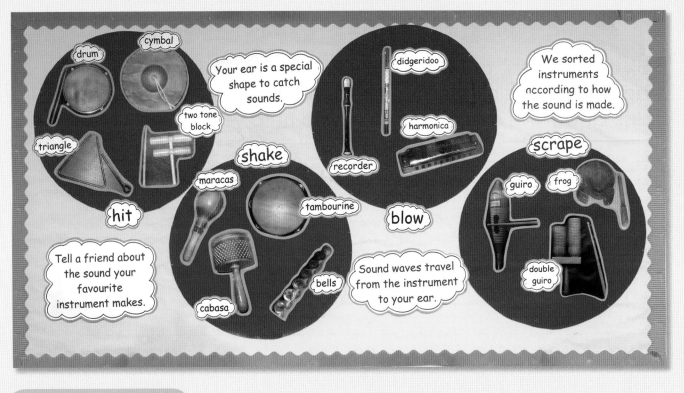

Music

- Sit the children in a circle. Ask them to pass a bag around the circle as a piece of music is played. When the music stops, the person holding the bag must take out an object from the bag and use their voice or body percussion to produce a suitable sound for the object. The bag could contain, for example, a selection of small toy animals or laminated pictures of everyday items.

- Play a mystery sound game, using a sound tape or CD. Ask the children to identify what is making the sound being played. This sound might be a dripping tap, footsteps, the hum of a microwave, for example.

- Play a guess-the-sound game. Ask children to play one from a selection of instruments behind a screen. The remaining children must listen carefully to the sound and guess which instrument has been used to make it. Encourage the children to make as many different sounds with the instrument as possible.

- Ask a small number of children to sit behind a screen, each with one different instrument. Ask these children to all play their instruments simultaneously. Then repeat, but indicate to one child not to play their instrument whilst the other few children still play. Ask the children who are listening on the other side of the screen to name the instrument that was not played. Repeat, with other combinations of instruments being played and not played.

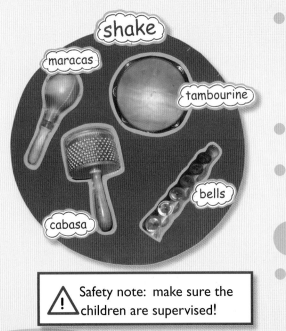

- Listen to 'March past of the kitchen utensils' by Ralph Vaughan Williams from *Listening to music elements* by Helen MacGregor and Alison Dextor (A & C Black Ltd). Experiment with making sounds using unusual objects. Challenge the children to compose and play a piece of music using unusual items such as kitchen utensils or other household objects.

- Sort different instruments according to the way they are played, as illustrated on the display here.

- Ask the children to play different instruments and represent the different sounds by symbols. Challenge the children to create a score of music using symbols as shown in the activity sheet.

PE

- Challenge the children, working in pairs, to navigate themselves through a series of low apparatus equipment, with one child blindfolded and reliant on listening to the instructions of their partner.

⚠ Safety note: make sure the children are supervised!

Sound & Hearing

What's the score?

Try playing each of the instruments shown below. Talk about the sounds you have made.

Now invent a sign or symbol to represent the sound. Draw your symbol next to the instrument.

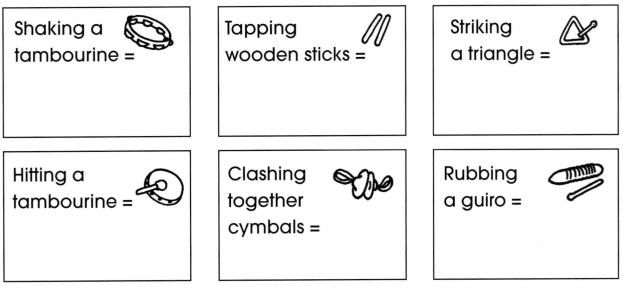

Shaking a tambourine =	Tapping wooden sticks =	Striking a triangle =
Hitting a tambourine =	Clashing together cymbals =	Rubbing a guiro =

Now use your symbols to create a score of music. This is called graphic notation.

1	2	3	4
5	6	7	8
9	10	11	12
13	14	15	16

**Practise your composition, following your score.
Perform your music to another class.**

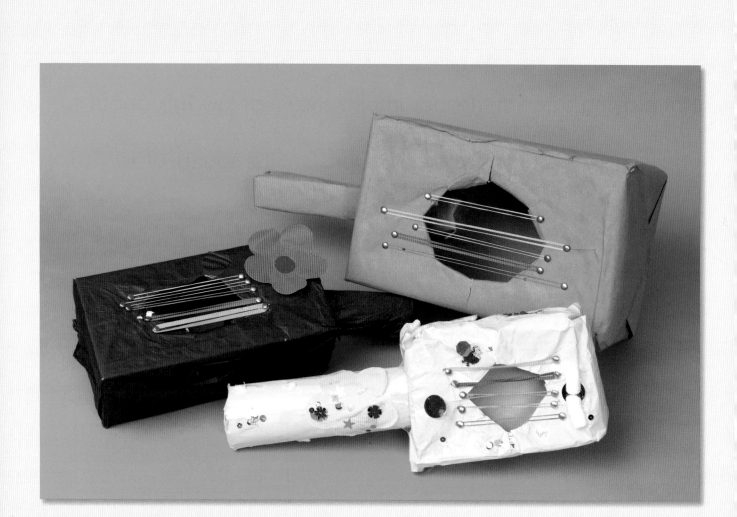

Design & Technology

- Look at and handle percussion and stringed instruments. Talk about how the sound is made and the quality of the sound produced.

- Create a simple stringed instrument using junk box materials and elastic bands. Challenge the children to be able to produce a stringed instrument that has a range of pitch.

- Create a simple percussion 'shaker' using plastic bottles and tubs with lids or with cardboard boxes. Use rice, lentils or dried pasta inside the shaker.

- Challenge the children to make an instrument similar to a 'rain stick', in which the contents of the shaker move gradually from one end to the other.

Art

- Provide the children with paper and a variety of mark-making media. Play a selection of music of differing genres and ask the children to respond to the music being played through drawing and mark making.

- Ask the children to make observational drawings of human ears.

- Take photographs of ears with a digital camera. Print and photocopy the resulting images and use as the basis for an imaginative collage consisting of ears.

- Look at a selection of artists' works that feature musical instruments. This could include *Music table* by Jock MacInnes (b. 1943), *Still life of fruit and musical instruments* by Antonio Pereda y Salgado (1611–1678) and *Still life with musical instruments* by Pieter Roestraten (1629–1700). Talk about the use of colour and composition with the children. Ask them to talk about which image they prefer and why.

Helen Keller 1880 1968
sound and hearing

She was born in Tuscumbia, Alabama, U.S.A.

In 1893 she went to a school for the deaf.

She became famous for helping other deaf people.

Helen Keller is a famous person from the past.

She had a special teacher called Anne Sullivan.

She was born in 1880.

She became deaf and blind in 1882 after an illness.

She met the American President, Herbert Hoover in 1932.

Helen Keller died in 1968.

Geography

- Find out about musical instruments from around the world, using the Internet and reference books. If possible, handle and play instruments from other countries. Locate these countries on a globe or map.

- Challenge the children to match instruments to the country of their origin. You could include castanets, bagpipes, a sitar, a didgeridoo, steel drums, a djembe drum, a balalaika and a caxixi. Locate these places on a large map of the world.

- Listen to pieces of music from around the world. Ask the children if they have been to any of the places featured in the musical excerpts. Create a fact file about a particular country.

History

- Find out about the life and times of Thomas Edison (1847–1931), who invented the phonograph in 1877. This invention was capable of recording and reproducing sound.

- Talk about Helen Keller (1880–1968), who was an American author and lecturer. Her life is described on the display here. A childhood illness left her deaf and blind but she learnt to read using Braille, and was the first deaf and blind person to graduate from college. She helped other people with disabilities and founded an organisation to help prevent blindness.

PSHCE

- Discuss with the class how very important it is not to insert items into the ear.

- Talk about noise safety levels and why people in certain occupations have to wear ear defenders to protect their ears from noise.

- Find out which children have had their ears examined or have had a hearing test. Ask these children to share their experiences.

- Invite the school nurse to come and talk about our sense of hearing.

- Talk about hearing loss and people who are deaf. Try to imagine living in a world without sound.

Light & Dark

These grids demonstrate the learning objectives covered in the activities within the theme. The curriculum references indicate the relevant programme of study (PoS) for a subject area unless otherwise stated.

	Learning Objectives	Curriculum References
Science (Page 54)		
Scientific Enquiry	Discuss ways in which a problem about reflection and light could be solved.	Sc1 2a
	Make first-hand observations when testing, make comparisons between materials.	Sc1/2b,h
	Communicate findings in an organised way.	Sc1/2g
Physical Processes (QCA Science Unit 1D)	Identify sources of light.	Sc4/3a
	Understand that absence of light causes darkness.	Sc4/3b
Materials and Their Properties	Sort materials according to a given criterion such as reflectivity.	Sc3/1b
Literacy (Page 56)		
Drama	Act out well known stories featuring light and dark scenarios.	En1/4a,b;11b
Speaking	Retell stories using story language.	En1/1b;1c,d
Engaging with and Responding to Texts	Select and read books about light and dark.	En2/3c;6b
	Make links between story events and own experiences.	En2/3a
Creating and Shaping Texts	Plan and write stories and poems about nocturnal animals.	En3/1b,c;2b
	Use a known story as a framework for own texts.	En3/1f
	Write captions for a photo story using digital images.	En3/1b,c; ICT PoS 5b
Mathematics (Page 58)		
Using and Applying Mathematics	Solve problems about birthday candles involving counting and addition.	Ma2/1a,c
	Create and describe repeating patterns.	Ma2/2b
	Use practical materials to find a solution to a light and dark shape puzzle.	Ma2/1b,g
Measuring	Use correct vocabulary when talking about time.	Ma3/4a
Understanding Shape	Name and describe 3-D shapes.	Ma3/2b
	Recognise reflective symmetry.	Ma3/2d
Handling Data	Organise and sort objects according to light source criteria.	Ma2/5a

Light & Dark

Learning Objectives	Curriculum References
History (Page 60)	
Observe and handle artefacts of things that make light.	PoS 4a
Place items in chronological order.	PoS 1a
Ask and answer questions about a famous person from the past, such as Thomas Edison.	PoS 4b/6c
Geography (Page 60)	
Use a plan of the school to locate 'dark places'.	PoS 2c
Use maps of the local area, locate places.	PoS 2c/4a
Describe a specific location.	PoS 3a
Compare places against each other.	PoS 3d/4a
Design & Technology (Page 62)	
Disassemble everyday objects such as a torch and discuss how they work.	PoS 5a
Generate ideas through investigating products.	PoS 1a
Design and create a kaleidoscope.	PoS 1e/2a,c,d/5c
Art (Page 62)	
Evaluate the works of known artists that depict sources of light.	PoS 4a,c
Interpret an artist's work through different media.	PoS 2c/5c
Music (Page 62)	
Listen to and discuss recorded music that suggests sources of light and dark.	PoS 4a
Play percussion instruments.	PoS 1b,c
Compose and perform music.	PoS 2a,b
Use graphic notation to record a score.	PoS 4c
Take account of musical elements such as timbre.	PoS 4b
PSHCE (Page 63)	
Identify ways of keeping safe with reflecting clothing.	PoS 3g
Discuss safety in the dark with a road safety officer.	PoS 5e
RE (Page 63)	
For a variety of religions, read and re-tell stories featuring light and dark.	PoS 1a/3f
Observe and celebrate a festival, such as Christingle.	PoS 1b/3g
Consider the symbolism of darkness and light.	PoS 1d
PE (Page 63)	
Respond to a musical stimulus to depict sunrise and sunset.	PoS 6a
Tell a story through dance.	PoS 6a,c
Work imaginatively with a partner to create a 'human mirror'.	PoS 6a,d

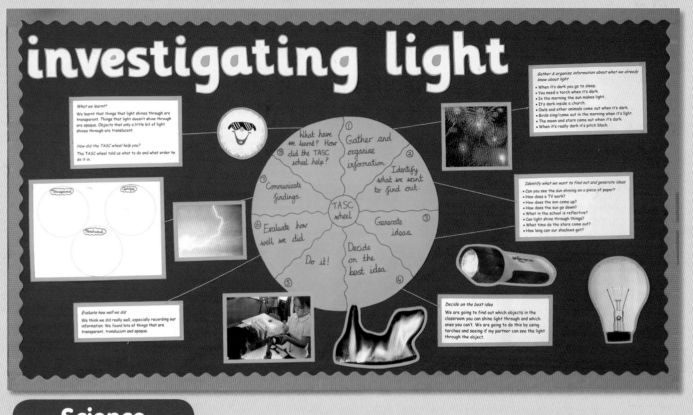

Science

Starting Points

● Ask the children to name sources of light, such as the sun, stars, fire, a candle, a torch, a bedside lamp and a television. Start a collection of items in your classroom. Distinguish between items that produce light and items that reflect light, such as the moon, glitter, a metal spoon and aluminium foil. Items that either produce or reflect light are shown here in the display.

Enquiry

● Present this scenario to the children: *It's Christmas Eve and Santa has discovered that Rudolph's nose has stopped glowing! Oh no! Without Rudolph's nose as a light source, Santa will find it difficult to navigate his sleigh in the darkness of the night sky. He will need your help to find something that is really shiny to wrap around Rudolph's nose, to reflect the moonlight, until Rudolph's glow returns.* Ask the children to think of a way that they could find out which material would be the best to use. Discuss and share ideas together. Ask the children to make predictions about which will be the least and the most reflective materials. Show the children a collection of materials, such as black felt fabric, greaseproof paper, foil, cling film, gift wrap and red wool, as shown on the activity sheet on page 55. Provide the children with a torch to shine onto the different items that are to be tested. Suggest that they could rank the different materials in order from least shiny to most shiny, and present the results in a strip or as a table to give to Santa.

Extension Activities

● Make a collection of shiny, reflective items such as metal objects, mirrors, glitter, tinsel, baubles and foil.

● Make a very simple periscope by attaching a small hand mirror to a metre stick, using a bulldog clip and ask the children to use it to see over the top of tall items or around corners.

● Allow the children to play and experiment with a collection of small hand mirrors. Can they use a mirror to see objects that are behind them, as with the internal mirror of a car? Can they produce multiple images of one object by placing it in the middle of several mirrors?

Rudolph's nose!

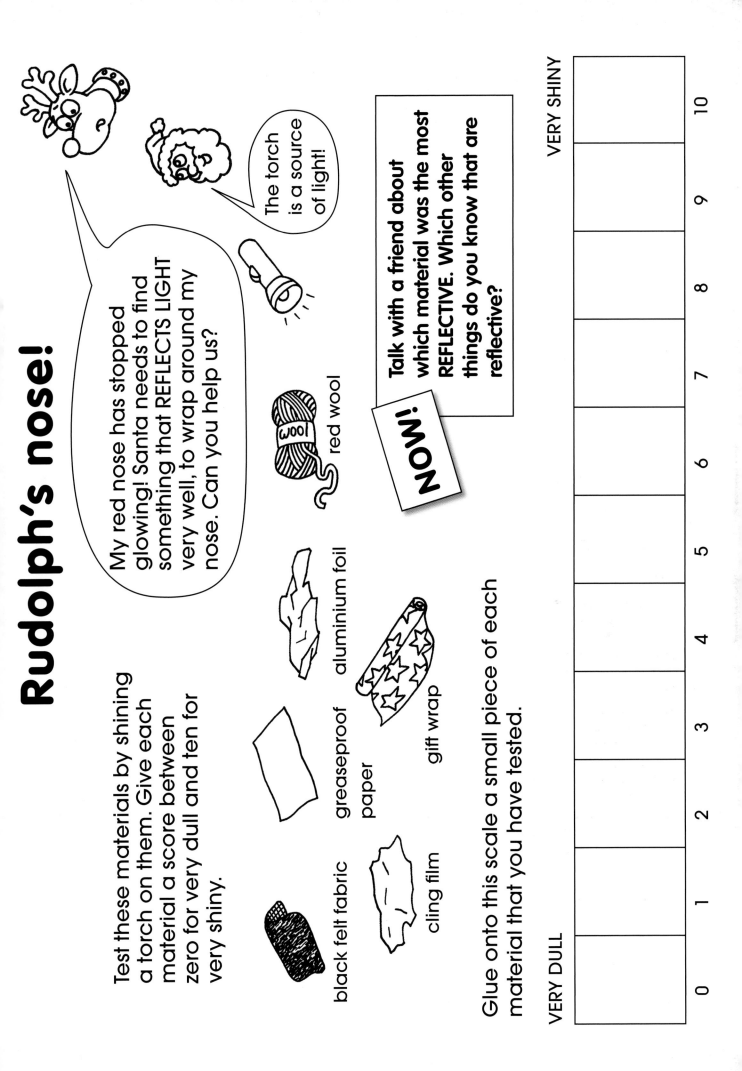

My red nose has stopped glowing! Santa needs to find something that REFLECTS LIGHT very well, to wrap around my nose. Can you help us?

The torch is a source of light!

Test these materials by shining a torch on them. Give each material a score between zero for very dull and ten for very shiny.

black felt fabric

cling film

greaseproof paper

aluminium foil

gift wrap

red wool

NOW!

Talk with a friend about which material was the most REFLECTIVE. Which other things do you know that are reflective?

Glue onto this scale a small piece of each material that you have tested.

VERY DULL

0	1	2	3	4	5	6	7	8	9	10

VERY SHINY

Literacy

Speaking and Listening

● Create a bear's cave in your class role play area. Use the cave as a setting for re-telling and acting out the story *We're going on a bear hunt* by Michael Rosen and Helen Oxenbury (Walker Books). Encourage the children to use language contained in the story such as the repetitive phrases that occur throughout the story. Hold a performance of this story for another class to watch.

Reading and Writing

● Read fiction books such as *The owl who was afraid of the dark* by Jill Tomlinson and Paul Howard (Egmont Books), *Don't be afraid of the dark* by Nancy Inteli (Simon Spotlight) and *Owl babies* by Martin Waddell and Patrick Benson (Walker Books).

● Read the story *Can't you sleep, little bear?* by Martin Waddell (Walker Books) and ask the children to talk about their own experiences of being afraid in the dark. Compare their experiences with those of story characters. Ask the children to write a list of things that the character of little bear could do if he is still afraid of the dark.

● Read the poem *In a dark, dark house* by Jennifer A. Dussling and Davy Jones (Grosset & Dunlap).

● Read non-fiction texts such as *My world of science: light and dark* by Angela Royston (Heinemann Library).

● Write a story about a nocturnal animal such as an owl, a bat or a fox. Use the owl story activity sheet on page 57 or use a digital camera and a toy owl to create a photo story and ask the children to write captions for the photos.

● Create and display a word bank for the light and dark topic in your classroom. Include words such as bright, dim, sparkle, glare, shine, shiny, dusk, shadow, dawn, glow, gleam. The words could be the basis for a class poem about light and dark or be included in the glossary of a class-made big book about light and dark.

● Sing the traditional nursery rhyme *Twinkle twinkle little star*, then as a class write a rhyme of your own about another light source, set to the same tune.

● Use a word processing package to type and print out labels for a collection of light and dark artefacts.

Light & Dark

Talk about what is happening in each picture. Cut out the pictures and stick them onto a strip of paper. Write a caption for each picture to tell the story.

NOW! Act out the story with a group of your friends.

Maths

Using and Applying

● Ask the children to create repeating patterns from images such as stars, moons and suns. Use the activity sheet on page 59 or use objects for the children to manipulate into a repeated pattern on a table top.

● Investigate the 'Birthday Cake Candles' problem. Challenge the children to calculate how many birthday cake candles they have had in their lifetime. Ask them to talk about ways in which they could find out the answer, such as by drawing pictures or by using real birthday cake candles and by using repeated addition. For instance, a child who is six years old would have had $1 + 2 + 3 + 4 + 5 + 6 = 21$ candles in their lifetime.

● Provide the children with two dark-coloured squares and two light-coloured squares and ask them to find out how many different ways the squares can be arranged. Then try four squares of each colour, then eight.

Measuring

● Use the context of light and dark as a springboard for work on the concept of time. Discuss the number of hours in a day, and the activities that we do during the daytime and at night.

● Make a classroom display about daylight and night-time hours as shown in the display.

Understanding Shape

● Use a collection of candles as part of work on 3-D shapes. Candles can be cylindrical, cuboidal or pyramidal in shape.

● Introduce work on symmetry through producing reflective images using black and white paper, along a single horizontal or vertical line of symmetry.

Handling Data

● Use sorting hoops to organise items into categories such as 'a light source' and 'not a light source'. Overlap two hoops to create a large Venn diagram to sort objects into 'see-through', 'partially see-through' and 'not see-through' groups.

Light & Dark

Repeating patterns

Can you draw the missing sections of these repeating patterns?

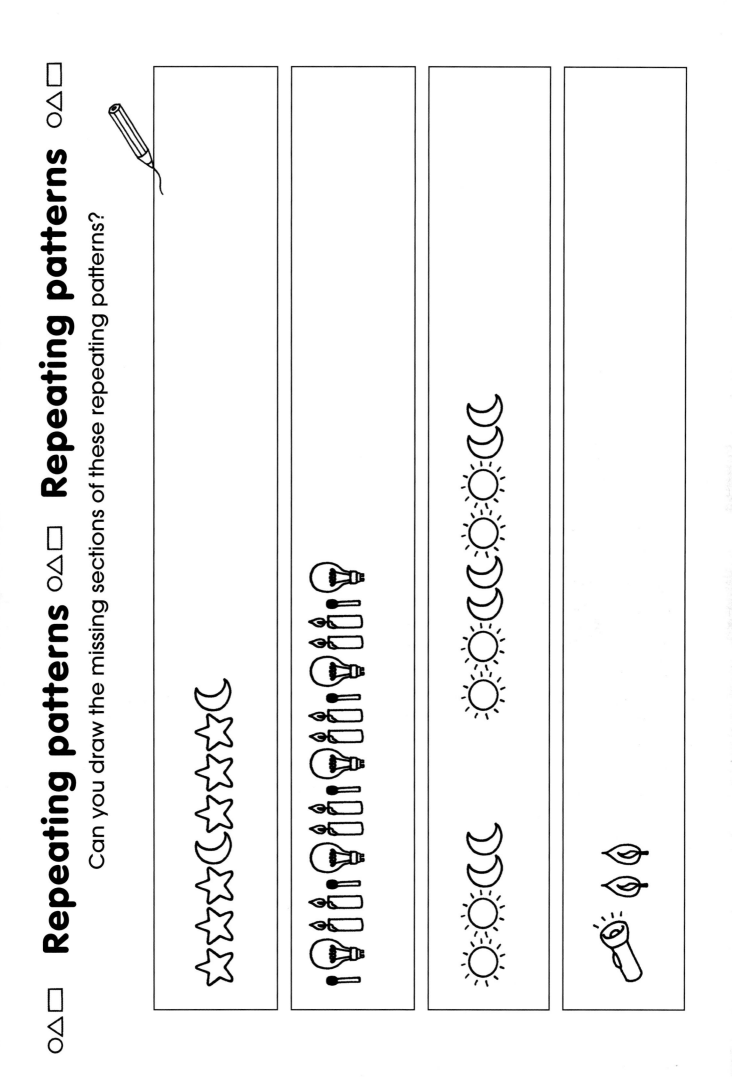

History

- Make a classroom collection of things that make light such as light bulbs, torches, lanterns, oil lamps, candles and candlesticks. Allow the children to handle and discuss the items in the collection. Ask them to sort the items into simple categories such as 'old' and 'new' and use this as a starting point for work on how people who lived in the past lit their homes and places of work. Items used to produce light in the past or in the present are shown here in the display photograph.

- Ask the children to place the items above in chronological order, creating a visual and tactile 'light' timeline.

- Light a candle in the classroom. Talk about the advantages and disadvantages of candlelight. Discuss candle safety.

- Find out some facts about Thomas Edison (1847–1931), who invented the light bulb in 1879.

- Compare a light bulb and a candle using the activity sheet on page 61.

Geography

- Show the children photographic images of different places and geographical features such as a hilltop, the seabed, a thickly wooded area, a cave formed in chalk cliffs, a valley, a railway tunnel, a wide sandy beach. Ask the children to compare the places with each other and to describe what they are like. Encourage the idea of a sense of place. Ask the children to sort the photographic images into 'dark' and 'light' places. Ask them to provide simple explanations for why the places are as they are.

- Ask the children to locate places on a map of the local area where the photographic images may have been taken, or begin a similar photographic collection using images of the locality.

- Create an underground cave or tunnel in your role play area. Encourage the children to describe what the cave is like.

- Go on a hunt for 'dark places' in the school building and grounds. Highlight where these places are located using a large plan of the school layout.

Now and then

Compare these two sources of light.

LIGHT BULB	CANDLE

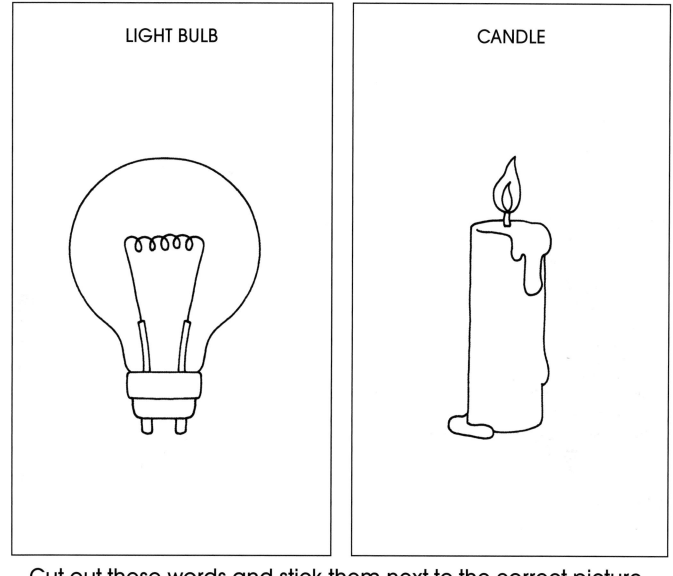

Cut out these words and stick them next to the correct picture.

wax	matches	filament	electric	old
new	flame	switch	glass	wick

NOW! **Talk about other sources of light from in the past and in the modern day.**

Design & Technology

- Disassemble a torch and allow the children to handle the component parts. Challenge the children to see if they can alter and improve a torch, for instance by adding a colourful strap or with the addition of a coloured cellophane 'filter' over the front.

- Look at and play with a collection of kaleidoscopes. Ask the children to assemble a simply made kaleidoscope of their own. Decorate a cardboard tube with felt pens or paint, tip in some sequins and attach cellophane at the ends of the tube with an elastic band.

- Look at a collection of sunglasses. Show the children some photographic images of 'celebrities' wearing sunglasses, including for instance Dame Edna Everage. Challenge the children to design and make a new pair of sunglasses for Dame Edna, or a celebrity of their choice. Ask the children to see who can use card, coloured cellophane, glitter, sequins and stars to make the most glamorous and outrageous pair! Evaluate the sunglasses in a class catwalk fashion parade!

Art

- Ask the children to look at a copy of the painting *Starry night* by Vincent Van Gogh (1853–1890). Encourage them to talk about colour, texture and brushwork.

- Using a print of *Starry night* as a starting point, ask the children to create their own starry night pictures using soft and smudgy pastel work.

- Ask the children to collaborate on a large, textured collage interpretation of *Starry night* using fabrics or tissue paper as shown here in the display photograph.

Music

- Listen to recorded music suggestive of sunrise, sunset, light and dark such as 'Morning' from the *Peer Gynt Suite* by Edvard Grieg (1843–1907) (Naxos), *Clair de Lune* by Claude Debussy (1862–1918) (Naxos) and *Chanson de Matin* and *Chanson de Nuit* by Edward Elgar (1857–1934) (Naxos).

- Ask the children to play percussion instruments such as the Indian bells and triangles when composing music suggesting light. Discuss the timbre of the sounds created.

- Combine individual ideas to create a piece of music that could be transcribed with graphic notation. Perform the piece to an audience.

- Sing popular songs with the theme of light such as *You are my sunshine* and *I can sing a rainbow*.

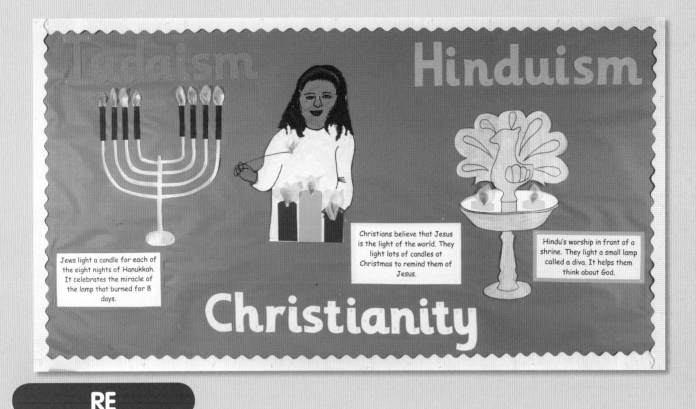

Judaism

Hinduism

Christians believe that Jesus is the light of the world. They light lots of candles at Christmas to remind them of Jesus.

Jews light a candle for each of the eight nights of Hanukkah. It celebrates the miracle of the lamp that burned for 8 days.

Hindu's worship in front of a shrine. They light a small lamp called a diva. It helps them think about God.

Christianity

RE

- Invite the local vicar into the class to talk about why Jesus is known as the 'Light of the World' and why candles are lit in churches.
- Find out how light is used in religions other than Christianity, for example those shown here in the display.
- Find out about the Christian festival Christingle. Make a Christingle using an orange, red ribbon, a candle and dried fruits.
- Read the traditional Hindu story of Rama and Sita. Use role play to re-tell the story.
- Hold a Diwali celebration with special food and lights.

PSHCE

- Show the children a high visibility jacket, such as that worn by the emergency services, refuse collectors, cyclists or by people who work outside at night. Explain why such jackets are worn and how they keep people safe.
- Ask a local road safety officer to come in and talk to the children about wearing bright coloured clothing when walking in the dark, for example when walking home from school in the darker winter months, and how this can make you more visible to traffic. The road safety officer may have access to free reflective strips, which could be distributed to the children to attach to their coats or bags.

PE

- Use music as such *Carnival of the animals: introduction and royal march of the lions* by Camille Saint-Saëns (1835–1921) (Sony) to prompt ideas for movement phrases and dance sequences to represent the sunrise. *Carnival of the animals: aquarium* (Sony) could be used as a stimulus for a twinkling stars dance. The 'John Dunbar theme' from *Dances with wolves* by John Barry (b. 1933) (Sony) could be used to evoke the idea of people or animals slowing down at the end of the day, moonrise and going to sleep, which could become the basis of a dance performance. *Recuerdos de la Alhambra* by Francisco Tárrega (1852–1909) (NCA) could be used to accompany a dance about feeling dozy and lazy in warm sunshine.
- Children working in pairs could perform movements in which one child is the other one's reflection in an imaginary mirror. Encourage movements at different heights and using different body parts. Allow the children time to take turns at being the 'reflection'.
- Use dance as a medium for telling a story, such as the traditional Hindu story of Rama and Sita.

Pushes & Pulls

These grids demonstrate the learning objectives covered in the activities within the theme. The curriculum references indicate the relevant programme of study (PoS) for a subject area unless otherwise stated.

	Learning Objectives	Curriculum References
Science (Page 66)		
Scientific Enquiry	Investigate pushes and pulls through testing and first-hand experience. Make measurements and record outcomes. Give possible reasons for what has occurred.	Sc1/1a;2a,b,c,h
Physical Processes (QCA Science Unit 1E)	Understand that pushes and pulls are forces.	Sc4/2b
	Explore how pushes and pulls can move objects, sort objects accordingly.	Sc4/2a
	Recognise that a push or pull can change the speed or direction of an object.	Sc4/2c; ICT PoS 2a
Materials and Their Properties	Explore how materials can be pushed, pulled and stretched. Investigate the elasticity of materials.	Sc3/2a
Literacy (Page 68)		
Speaking	Read stories about pushes and pulls out aloud.	En1/1a;3a
Drama	Participate in role play and drama activities.	En1/11b
	Speak to an audience in role.	En1/11a
Engaging with and Responding to Texts	Read a variety of fiction texts about pushes and pulls.	En2/2c;6e
Understanding and Interpreting Texts	Sequence story events in correct order.	En2/3b
	Use knowledge of stories to predict endings and outcomes.	En2/1m;3b
Creating and Shaping Texts	Plan and write stories and poems about pushes and pulls.	En3/2c,d
	Use organisational features to structure writing.	En3/1d
Mathematics (Page 70)		
Counting and Understanding Number	Estimate then count objects.	Ma2/2a
	Place objects into multiples of five or ten before counting.	Ma2/1g;2b
	Read and write numbers.	Ma2/2c
Measuring	Use equipment such as tape measures, rulers and metre sticks to measure and record the length of objects and distances.	Ma3/4c
	Use standard units of measurement.	Ma3/4a
Handling Data	Use tables, charts and apparatus to sort items and information.	Ma2/5a

Learning Objectives	Curriculum References
Design & Technology (Page 72)	
Evaluate made products through play.	PoS 5a
Use first-hand experience to generate design ideas.	PoS 1a/4b
Draw and follow a design for a play park.	PoS 1d,e
Create objects by joining materials together.	PoS 2a,c,d
Evaluate own product against the original design criteria.	PoS 3a,b
PSCHE (Page 72)	
Understand basic safety posed by heavy, moving objects.	PoS 3g
Work co-operatively with others to achieve a desirable result.	PoS 4b
Art (Page 74)	
Use a variety of stimuli, including music and still images, as a starting point for printing.	PoS 1b/5a
Record by observational drawing.	PoS 1a
Experiment with tools and techniques when creating printed images.	PoS 2b;5c
Music (Page 74)	
Experiment with and play percussion instruments.	PoS 1b;2b;4c
Work collaboratively to produce and perform music.	PoS 1c;3b
Listen with attentiveness to a selection of orchestral music.	PoS 4a
Show understanding of how music can be used to create mood and effect.	PoS 4d
History (Page 75)	
Examine artefacts from the past and identify how these push and pull toys were different to the modern equivalent.	PoS 2b
Recognise the reasons behind events and activities in the past.	PoS 2a;6b
Geography (Page 75)	
Ask questions in order to obtain a sense of place.	PoS 1a/3a
Locate features, such as windmills, on a map.	PoS 3b
Research information from a variety of sources.	PoS 2d
PE (Page 75)	
Use a musical stimuli to construct and perform a dance sequence.	PoS 6a-d
Develop and perform skills involving movement and travelling.	PoS 8a,b
Identify and discuss how their bodies are moving in PE.	PoS 4b

Pushes & Pulls

Science

Starting Points

● Play with push and pull toys. Make a class toy collection. How do they work, how are they moved?

● Play with toy windmill or a water-play set that includes a water mill.

● Experiment with pushing and pulling malleable or stretchy materials and objects such as dough, Blu-Tack®, elastic, rubber bands, nylon tights, balloons, fabrics, cling film, plastic carrier bags.

● Describe different activities that use pushing or pulling, such as those shown here in the display photograph.

Enquiry

● Carry out the Tumbling Ted investigation as shown on the activity sheet on page 67. Pose questions such as 'Does the distance we pull the elastic back increase the distance that Ted is pushed forward when the elastic is released?' Allow time for the children to talk about what they think is going to happen.

● Using a large space such as an assembly hall, set up a chair at one end, with a loop of elastic tied around two of the chair legs. Arrange metre sticks in a line to record the distance travelled and sit the children in two lines, facing each other, forming a 'corridor' in which Ted will travel. Use chalk or tape to mark out on the floor the distance that the elastic is being pulled back. Try out the experiment three times and ask the children to measure and record the distance that Ted travels. Then repeat, with the elastic pulled back further, to 10cm, then again to 15cm. Introduce the idea of creating a fair test by pointing out to the children the things that are staying the same and that only the amount of pull back on the elastic is changing. Children could use a digital camera to record what happens and printed out images could be added to their written work later, or record events using a digital movie camera.

● Create a simple table of results in a word processing program. Encourage the children to talk about anything they notice about the relationship between how far the elastic is pulled back and how far Ted is propelled forward. What has happened and why? Did anyone make an accurate prediction before the test was carried out? See the display on page 70 for more ideas using this investigation.

Extension Activities

● The children could look at and try out small hand-held catapults in the playground. Who can make a small object, such as a ball of scrunched-up paper, travel the furthest?

● Can the children think of a way in which pulling on an elastic material to create a push in the opposite direction could be used in a real life situation?

Tumbling Ted!

How far can you make Ted travel? Does pulling the elastic band further make a difference? Try it out!

YOU NEED: a loop of elastic   a chair!   a plastic teddy   metre sticks   ...and a space in the hall or corridor!

RECORD YOUR FINDINGS HERE:

Pull the elastic back ... then let go!	first attempt	second attempt	third attempt
pull back (5 cm)	Ted travelled .... cm	Ted travelled .... cm	Ted travelled .... cm
pull back (10 cm)	Ted travelled .... cm	Ted travelled .... cm	Ted travelled .... cm
pull back (15 cm)	Ted travelled .... cm	Ted travelled .... cm	Ted travelled .... cm

NOW! Talk about what happened! What have you found out about pushes and pulls?

Literacy

Speaking and Listening

● Ask the children to talk about and list things that are pushed and pulled to make them move. Use the words and ideas generated as a basis for a whole-class poem or song about forces.

● Ask children, acting in the roles of TV news presenters, to talk about their pushes and pulls work to the headteacher.

● Use role play to act out the story.

Reading and Writing

● Read stories that include an element of pushing or pulling in the action, such as *The enormous turnip* by Jan Lewis (Ladybird), *The last noo-noo* by Jill Murphy (Walker Books), or 'Pooh goes visiting' from *Winnie the Pooh* by A.A. Milne (Methuen). Marlon and his noo-noo (dummy) are shown here in the display where the pushes and pulls are labelled.

● Use the Kim's Kite activity sheet on page 69 as a framework for story writing. Encourage lots of discussion about the ending of the story.

● Ask the children to plan and write their own story about the character Kim, with a different pushing or pulling element creating the climax of the story.

● Read non-fiction texts such as *Find out about pushes and pulls* by Terry Jennings (BBC Books). Use the contents page to pick out information relevant to your needs.

Pushes & Pulls

Kim's kite

Talk about what is happening in each picture.

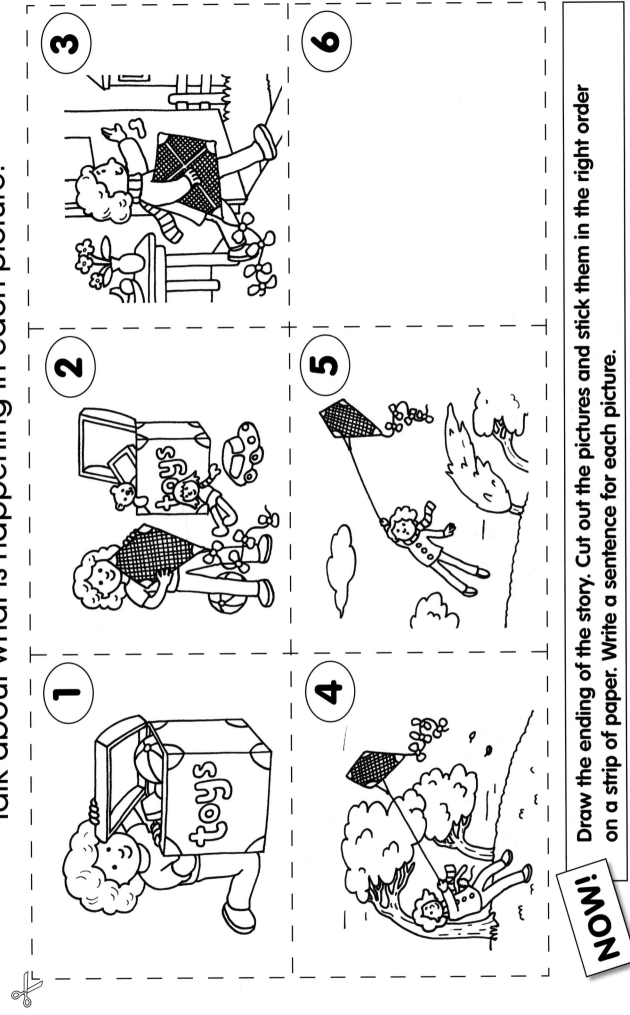

Maths

Understanding Number

● When collecting stretchy objects, place a quantity of unused balloons in a sealed container such as a screw-top plastic jar. Ask children to estimate how many balloons they think are inside. Leave a large sheet of paper and pens next to the jar for the children to write down their estimates. A prize could be awarded for the closest estimate. When counting out the balloons, put them into piles of five or ten first to rehearse counting in these steps.

● Ask the children to estimate how many push or pull activities that they can do in one minute, such as bouncing a ball or pulling Christmas crackers. Write down the estimates then try the activities out, with children operating a stopwatch.

Measuring

● Use appropriate measuring equipment to measure the distance travelled in the Tumbling Ted investigation on page 67. Note down the measurements, for example as illustrated here in the display photograph.

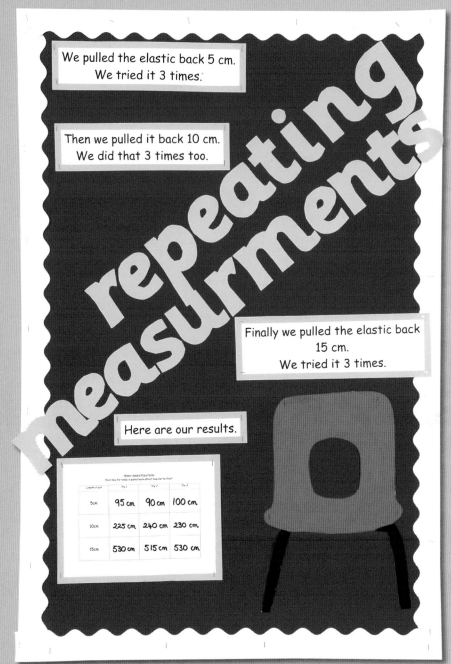

● Measure a pair of nylon tights, before and after stretching them, using the activity shown on page 71. Ask the children to use either counting on or subtraction as a strategy to calculate the difference between the two measurements.

Handling Data

● Use sorting hoops to sort objects such as toys into categories with criteria such as 'push' and 'pull'.

● Encourage the children to use a ruler to measure and mark out component pieces when constructing play-park models.

● Use metre sticks laid out along the ground to measure the distance travelled by an object when flung using a catapult. Ask the children to record the measurements in metres and centimetres, explaining that 100 centimetres makes a metre.

● Conduct a survey about which item of playground or play-park equipment is the most popular. Demonstrate how to record raw data using a tally chart. Use the tally chart to create a simple bar graph, then ask the children to look at their graph to answer questions about the data such as, *How many more people prefer the tyre swings than the roundabout?*

Measuring Length

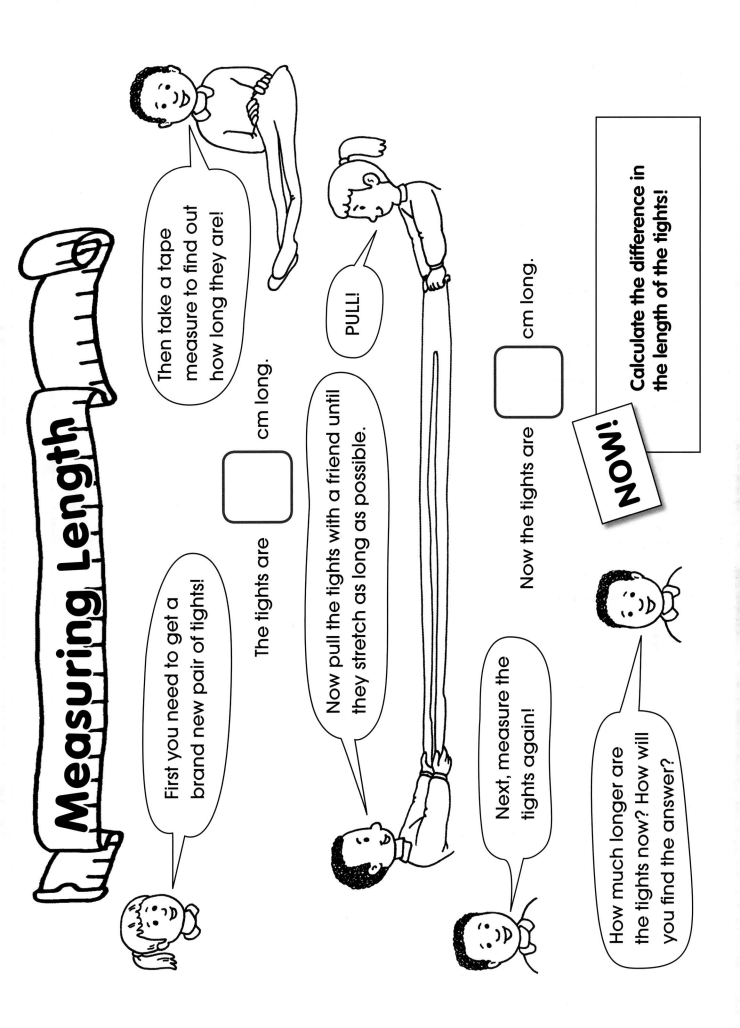

First you need to get a brand new pair of tights!

Then take a tape measure to find out how long they are!

The tights are ☐ cm long.

Now pull the tights with a friend until they stretch as long as possible.

PULL!

Now the tights are ☐ cm long.

NOW!

Calculate the difference in the length of the tights!

Next, measure the tights again!

How much longer are the tights now? How will you find the answer?

Design & Technology

- Visit a local park or play area and record, using a digital camera, the children's play equipment available. Make drawings of any adventure play equipment that you may have on your school playground. Investigate how the equipment, such as that on the activity sheet on page 73, has been put together and how moving parts work. Discuss preferences with the children. Which things are the most fun to play on?

- Ask the children to design and draw ideas for a model playpark. Using a selection of resources, including junk box materials, create a model of a children's playpark. Individual children could make separate models, contributing each to a collaborative effort. Evaluate the finished product. Assess whether it matches the design sketches.

- Look at and play with a selection of stringed puppets. Evaluate how well the puppets work.

- Look at a simple kite to discern how it has been made. Make a simple, small-scale kite from tissue and thread.

- Disassemble a child's toy windmill and then use as a template to create toy windmills of your own.

- Read *Mrs Armitage on wheels* by Quentin Blake (Random House). Discuss the pushes and pulls in the story and create a model bike to display in front of the children's writing about pushes and pulls.

PSHCE

- Discuss with the children the dangers posed by heavy, moving objects.

- Set groups of children a challenge, such as transporting a fragile object across a large space, which can only be achieved through teamwork and co-operation.

> ⚠ Safety note: make sure the children are supervised!

Pushes & Pulls

LOOK AT THE PLAY EQUIPMENT

see-saw

WHICH ONE IS YOUR FAVOURITE?

roundabout

·MAKE·DESIGN·AND·MAKE·DESIGN·AND·MAKE·DESIGN·AND·MAKE·DESIGN·AND·

At the park

monkey bars

HOW COULD YOU MAKE A MODEL OF IT?

WHAT WILL YOUR MODEL LOOK LIKE?

swings

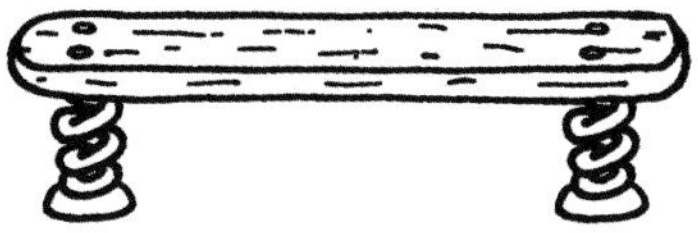

wobble board

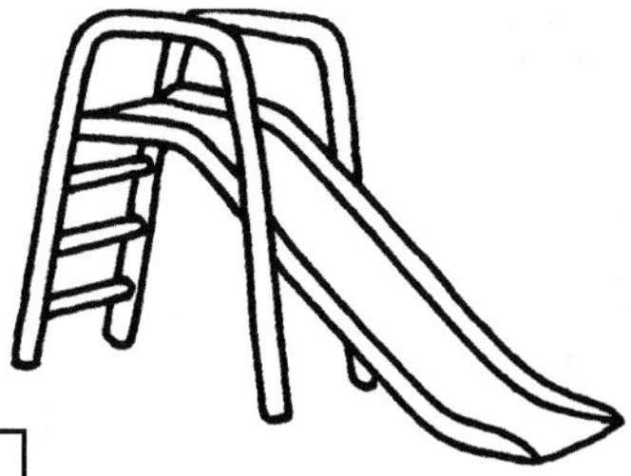

NOW!

slide

WHICH MATERIALS WILL YOU USE?

Talk about your ideas. Draw a picture of what you want your model to look like. Add labels to your design.

HOW WILL YOU FIX IT TOGETHER?

We used wheels to make our own pictures.

wonderful wheels

Art

- Print using objects such as wheels or cogs as tools. Experiment with mark-making possibilities. Create a display of the children's work.

- Make observational drawings of push and pull toys.

- Look at photographic images of windy weather as a starting point for creating a windy day picture using pastels or paint.

- Experiment with the different effects that can be achieved by applying differing amounts of force when pressing down an item.

- Press flowers collected from the school grounds or local gardens. Small, simple flowers such as pansies and daises work well. Press between the pages of a book. Place a heavy object onto the book to push down and press the flowers. After a week or two, collaged images can be created from the pressed flowers.

Music

- Listen to pieces of orchestral music that are representative of the movement of puppets such as *Puppet's dance* by William Walton (1902–1983) (Lyrita), *Concerto for trumpet and orchestra: puppets* movement by Will Todd (b. 1970) (Tyalgum) or *The puppet fairy* by Joseph Bayer (1852–1913) (Naxos). Discuss the effects created, express likes and dislikes.

- Listen to the 'autumn' section from *The four seasons* by Antonio Vivaldi (1678–1741) (EMI). Experiment with the variety of sounds that can be created with percussion instruments to produce appropriate sound effects for a windy weather piece, composed by the class. Select and combine sounds to compose a piece of music and perform it to another class. You could record your own piece of music and use it in PE as a stimulus for dance.

Pushes & Pulls

History

- Investigate how wind power and water power have been used in the past as natural sources of energy.

- Make a visit to a local watermill or windmill if you have one in your area.

- Make a 'virtual visit' on-line, using a website such as www.ukmills.com.

- Look at manufacturing industries from the past that were sited next to rivers to utilise the power of moving water.

- Discuss the reasons why wind and water power were relied upon in the past as a means to generate power. Identify how things have changed since then. What caused the changes?

- Compare moving toys from the past with modern toys today. Identify ways in which the toys are the same and are different.

- Make a visit to a local toy museum or start a class collection, using toys lent by parents and grandparents. Find toys that use pushes and pulls to move.

- Research information on old toys from a website such as www.pollocksmuseum.co.uk.

- Read *My toys, Gran's toys* by Nicola Tuxworth (Oxford Literacy Web). Both the boy's and his gran's toys are described here in the display photograph.

Geography

- Ask the children to consider what a windmill needs in order for it to work, this being the pushing force of the wind.

- Encourage the children to make the connection between the need for wind and the physical location of the windmill. Explain that windmills can be found on high ground or exposed areas.

PE

- Ask the children to work with a partner. One child is to move in the role of a puppet, controlled by the other child who is the puppeteer. The 'puppet' may only move their body and limbs when they are 'pulled' by the imaginary strings, held by the puppeteer.

- Rehearse the puppet movements and perform as a dance sequence, perhaps to a musical accompaniment such as *The puppet fairy* by Joseph Bayer (1852–1913) (Naxos).

- Listen to music from *The four seasons: autumn* by Antonio Vivaldi (1678–1741) (EMI) as a starting point for a dance about windy weather.

- Ask the children to perform basic skills and actions, such as hopping, skipping, bending or sliding, and focus their attention on how groups of muscles are pushing and pulling their body in order to execute the movement.

Assessment Ideas

In any activity the children carry out, whether through discussing, planning, doing or writing, there is an element of assessment. There are many ways to assess children – see the ideas below and the grid on page 77 for further suggestions. Knowledge-based assessments should use a variety of methods such as games, quizzes, drama and role play presentations, discussion of 'concept cartoons' and completing 'concept maps'.

- Concept cartoons are a useful tool in teaching and assessing. Each cartoon takes an everyday scientific idea about which three or more points of view are shown. For example, it could be a variety of views about how quickly objects fall. The cartoons encourage children to think carefully about what is being discussed and say which point of view they agree with and why. The cartoons generally portray a range of ideas which can be used to promote discussion of the children's own ideas and inform teachers what to teach and how to group children. For more information visit www.conceptcartoons.com

- Concept maps are also useful. The idea is to link nouns about a theme with arrows. The arrow shows the connection between the two words. For example:

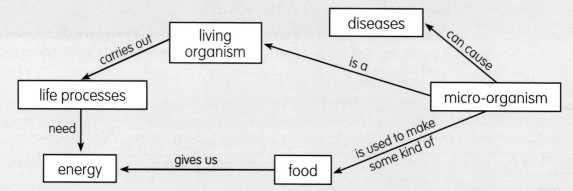

- Ensure that you have clear learning objectives for your lessons and that these are shared and understood by the children.

- Tell the children what the success criteria are and how they can achieve them.

- When marking children's work, highlight successes against the learning objective and write affirmative statements on the page such as 'you can make a circuit' or 'you can name parts of the body'.

- Include time for assessment work in your daily and weekly planning. You may wish to conduct an end of topic investigation to access the children's level of knowledge and understanding.

- At the end of the topic, create a spreadsheet document to record the children's attainment against the objectives. Colour-code the cells: red for not achieved, orange for objective met and green for those who have exceeded expectations. This will produce an 'at a glance' reference to achievement and will highlight areas that need further work. Such documents could be handed on with other record-keeping to inform planning in subsequent year groups.

- Self-assessment sheets for children to complete are included on pages 78–80. The sheets cover areas of knowledge taught throughout the year. Children should be given their own sheets at the end of teaching a theme for them to colour in the objectives achieved. These could be colour-coded for those areas they think they know well/are uncertain about/do not know. The 'I can ...' statements of skills will be practised in different contexts throughout the year, so children need to make judgements on each one more than once, again at the end of each theme and they should write the date in the column when the skill is achieved. Use all the sheets alongside your assessments to inform reports and general assessment at the end of the school year.

Who Should Assess?

- Anyone involved with children's learning can assess, including parents and the children themselves. The most important thing is that the assessor knows what they are looking for and has the skills and knowledge to make these judgements. Children can assess each other – but they should always try to be constructive – what are the good points as well as the not so good?

HOW	TIPS
Observation of Children Working	Use this method when there is no written work as evidence, for example, when children are planning and discussing. Assess a single child or a group by questioning the children to clarify understanding.
Group Feedback	Use this method to clarify the understanding of 'quiet' children or those you are unsure about. Allow the 'listening' children to ask questions of 'presenters'. Ask questions of the children to gain a greater understanding of their learning.
Recording Children's Views During an Activity	Gather the children's opinions and ideas during activities. Ask the children to make their own recordings for you to listen to after the lesson.
Drama	This method is fun and non-threatening for children as they can 'show' instead of write their understanding of key objectives. Use role play to discuss issues and act out events and imaginary situations such as, 'inside a part of the body', 'in space' or 'inside the Earth' to clarify understanding of key concepts.
Concept Cartoons	Use at the beginning and/or at the end of lessons to clarify children's ideas.
Diagrams, Drawings and Photographs	Ask the children to draw ideas before teaching and at the end to compare understanding of concepts. Make or interpret concept maps before and after lessonsor topics. Photograph the children's work before and after the topic is complete to compare.
Sort a Collection	Ask the children to sort a collection of objects/vocabulary related to the topic in different ways. This method is particularly good for Maths and Science, to pinpoint the children's grasp of skills and knowledge.
Make & Play a Game	Incorporate key concepts and vocabulary into games, for example, create questions that the children have to answer correctly before they move a space on a board game. Laminate games and retain for future use.
Devise & Answer Questions	Put questions in a box (generated by the teacher and the children) and ask the children to answer them over the course of the topic.
Interactive Display	Put questions on displays which highlight key concepts instead of labels. Add to the display as the topic progresses.
Types of Quiz	Create a true/false quiz on areas of knowledge and play this before and after teaching the topic to compare the children's responses. Quizzes can be oral or written by children or teacher.
Written Work	Writing is useful as evidence but be aware that this is not always the best way for children to demonstrate what they know or can do. Use different genres of writing.

Life Processes and Living Things

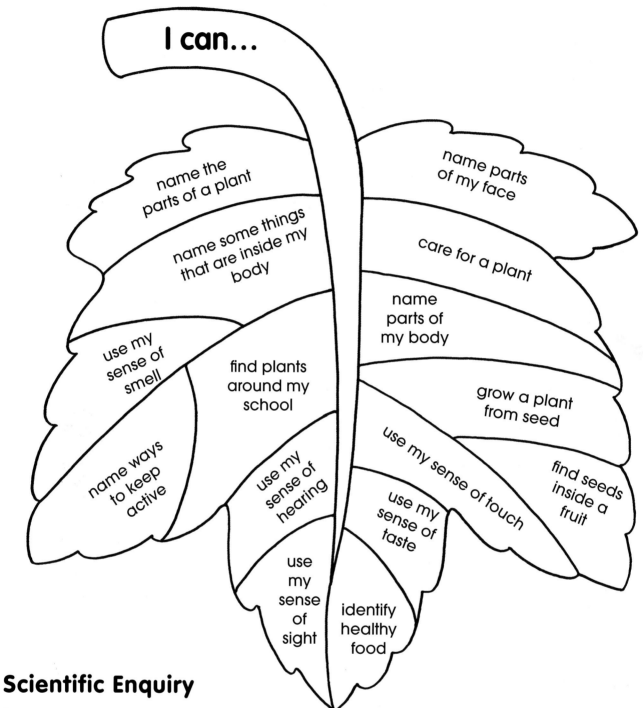

I can...

name the parts of a plant

name parts of my face

name some things that are inside my body

care for a plant

name parts of my body

use my sense of smell

find plants around my school

grow a plant from seed

name ways to keep active

use my sense of hearing

use my sense of touch

use my sense of taste

find seeds inside a fruit

use my sense of sight

identify healthy food

Scientific Enquiry

I can...

Skill	Date	Date	Date	Skill	Date	Date	Date
follow simple instructions				make observations and talk about what I have seen			
ask questions about the things around me				draw and label pictures			
talk about ways to find answers to questions				talk about what has happened to others			
talk about what might happen				make simple explanations			

Materials and Their Properties

I can...

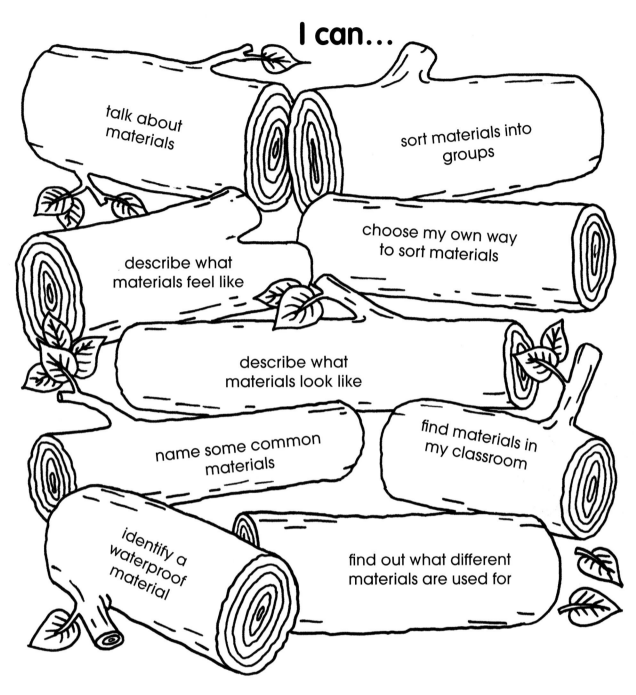

talk about materials

sort materials into groups

choose my own way to sort materials

describe what materials feel like

describe what materials look like

find materials in my classroom

name some common materials

identify a waterproof material

find out what different materials are used for

Scientific Enquiry

I can...

Skill	Date	Date	Date	Skill	Date	Date	Date
ask questions about the things around me				follow measures to keep a test fair			
share ideas with others				make observations and talk about what I have seen			
talk about ways to find answers to question				draw and label pictures			
make a simple prediction				talk about what has happened to others			

Physical Processes

I can...

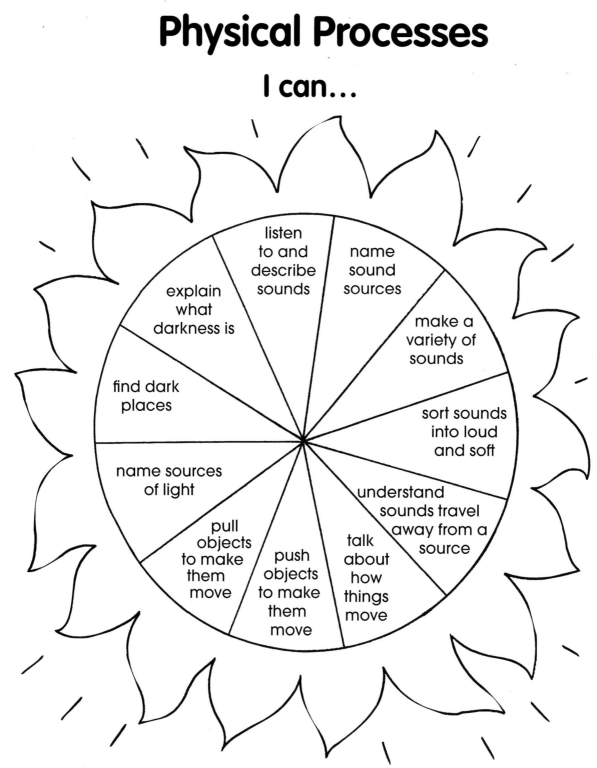

listen to and describe sounds

name sound sources

explain what darkness is

make a variety of sounds

find dark places

sort sounds into loud and soft

name sources of light

understand sounds travel away from a source

pull objects to make them move

push objects to make them move

talk about how things move

Scientific Enquiry

I can...

Skill	Date	Date	Date	Skill	Date	Date	Date
talk about my ideas and share them with others				work with others to investigate an idea			
decide how to answer questions				record simple measurements			
talk about what might happen				make observations and record them by drawing			
use equipment safely				talk to others about what has happened			